PARROT
FINCHES

PARROT FINCHES

The Aviculturist's Guide

Stewart Evans and
Mike Fidler

BLANDFORD

First published 1990 by **Blandford**
An imprint of Cassell
Artillery House, Artillery Row, London SW1P 1RT

Text Copyright © Stewart Evans and Mike Fidler 1990

Distributed in the United States by
Sterling Publishing Co, Inc,
387 Park Avenue South, New York, NY 10016-8810

Distributed in Australia by
Capricorn Link (Australia) Pty Ltd
PO Box 665, Lane Cove, NSW 2066

British Library Cataloguing in Publication Data

Evans, Stewart
  Parrot Finches
  1. Parrot Finches
  I. Title   II. Fidler, Mike
  598.8'83

ISBN 0-7137-2112-X

Typeset by Litho Link Limited, Welshpool, Powys, Wales
Printed and bound in Great Britain by Biddles Ltd., Guildford and King's Lynn

Contents

Acknowledgements

We would like to thank Dr Mike Coates for the drawings of parrot finches; Paul Holmes for the drawings of the mouth markings and the distribution maps; Val and Ron Moat for the photograph of the lutino Blue-faced Parrot Finch; Dennis Avon for all the other photographs of parrot finches; Audrey Morrow and Jackie Burnett for typing the manuscript; Stuart Booth and Rosie Anderson for help with editorial matters.

Preface

There is an increasing awareness among aviculturists of the need to establish more bird species in captivity. The present dependence on wild-trapped birds of many species for captive stock is not only unsatisfactory, but cannot last. Habitat destruction, and regrettably in some areas, bird trapping, is decimating natural populations of birds to such an extent that legislation to protect what remains of them in the wild is both desirable and inevitable. Paradoxically, aviculture can play a significant role in conserving endangered species, but it will only do so if serious attempts are made to develop suitable husbandry and captive management techniques for them.

The parrot finches are one of the groups of birds which deserve a secure place in aviculture. Their beautiful coloration, coupled with their engaging personalities and high levels of activity, make them excellent cage birds. Thanks to the efforts of a relatively small number of enthusiasts, they are well on their way to becoming established in captivity, but further research on them is needed. Our intention in writing this book is to stimulate this. We have attempted to produce a readable account of what is known about parrot finches in captivity and in the wild as a basis for further studies. Our own experience of the group includes keeping most of them in captivity, and observing some species under natural conditions.

We have, nevertheless, relied heavily on the experiences of others in acquiring knowledge of the parrot finches and are especially indebted to the research of Dr V. Ziswiler, Dr H.

Guttinger and Dr H. Bregulla. Their findings, which are described in a lengthy monograph in German, leave many questions unanswered, as they themselves would readily acknowledge, but their work will undoubtedly remain the standard scientific reference on parrot finches for many years.

Stewart Evans
Mike Fidler

1

The Genus *Erythrura*

Parrot finches belong to the family Estrildidae which includes, among others, waxbills, firefinches, cordon bleus and grass-finches. The family as a whole is distributed over most of Africa, Asia and Australia but does not occur naturally on either the European or the American continents. There are 11 species of parrot finches and their distribution covers only a small part of the family's range. They are restricted to the Indo-Pacific region, including countries such as Thailand, Borneo, Malaysia, Indonesia, the Philippines and New Guinea, and several of the groups of tiny islands in the Pacific Ocean.

What Is a Parrot Finch?

The origin of the name parrot finch is obscure since the birds have no relationship whatsoever to parrots. One possibility is that they were given the name because of the strongly bent ridge line of the upper mandible of the beak. Another is that their green-blue plumage is reminiscent of some parrots.

The first species known to science was the Pin-tailed Parrot Finch which was collected in Java and described by Sparrman in 1788. Discoveries of other species followed expeditions to the Indo-Pacific and Pacific islands and descriptions of their previously unknown faunas and floras. Thus, the Red-headed Parrot Finch was described by Gmelin in 1788 following its discovery in New Caledonia; Vieillot described the Blue-faced

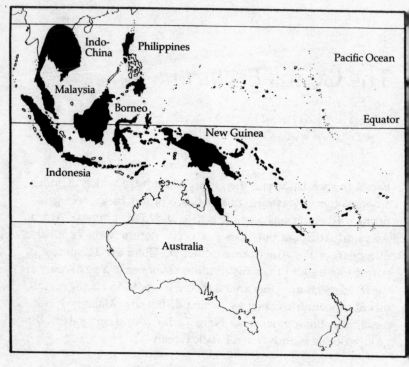

Fig. 1 The Indo-Pacific region and Pacific Ocean. Areas occupied by parrot finches are shown in black.

Parrot Finch in 1817, and so on. The most recent discovery was in 1960, when the Katanglad Parrot Finch was observed by R.B.Gonzales on the slopes of Mount Katanglad in the Philippines. It was described the following year in a paper by Ripley and Rabor (1961).

All 11 of the parrot finches are included in the genus *Erythrura*. Four of them have sub-species so that, at present, the following forms are recognized:

The Bamboo Finch, *Erythrura hyperythra*.
  Eight sub-species:
  E.h. brunneiventris
  E.h. borneensis

E.h. malayana

E.h. hyperythra

E.h. intermedia

E.h. obscura

E.h. microrhyncha

E.h. ernstmayri

The Pin-tailed Parrot Finch, *Erythrura prasina*.

 Two sub-species:

E.p. prasina

E.p. coelica

The Manila Parrot Finch, *Erythrura viridifacies*.

The Tri-coloured Parrot Finch, *Erythrura tricolor*.

The Blue-faced Parrot Finch, *Erythrura trichroa*.

Ten sub-species:

E.t. cyanofrons

E.t. sanfordi

E.t. modesta

E.t. pinaiae

E.t. sigillifera

E.t. eichhornis

E.t. palewensis

E.t. clara

E.t. trichroa

E.t. woodfordi

The Papuan Parrot Finch, *Erythrura papuana*

The Katanglad Parrot Finch, *Erythrura coloria*

The Red-headed Parrot Finch, *Erythrura psittacea*

Peale's Parrot Finch, *Erythrura pealii*

The Royal Parrot Finch, *Erythrura cyaneovirens*

Five sub-species:

E.c. cyaneovirens

E.c. regia

E.c. efatensis

E.c. serena

E.c. gaughrani

The Pink-billed Parrot Finch, *Erythrura kleinschmidti*

Table 1 The years in which parrot finches were first described, and the authorities who described them. Information from Ziswiler et al., 1972.

Year	Species	Authority
1788	Pin-tailed Parrot Finch	Sparrman
1789	Red-headed Parrot Finch	Gmelin
1817	Tri-coloured Parrot Finch	Vieillot
1835	Blue-faced Parrot Finch	Kittlitz
1848	Royal Parrot Finch (Vanuatu)	Sclater
1852	Peale's Parrot Finch	Hartlaub
1862-3	Bamboo Parrot Finch	Reichenbach
1878	Pink-billed Parrot Finch	Finsch
1881	Royal Parrot Finch (Samoa)	Peale
1900	Papuan Parrot Finch	Hartert
1937	Manila Parrot Finch	Hachisuka & Delacour
1961	Katanglad Parrot Finch	Ripley & Rabor

A unique feature of the parrot finches, which makes them special in the family Estrildidae, is that they have largely abandoned the grassland habitat which is typical of most African, Asian and Australian species. The parrot finches mostly live in association with tropical rain forests, although usually along the edges of the forests or in clearings in them.

The foods available to them in this habitat are different from those in grasslands, and there have been consequent changes in diet. Some parrot finches still rely on a staple diet of grass seeds, but some have become generalists, taking seeds of various herbaceous plants in their diets. Others have become specialist feeders on the fruits of forest plants, such as fig and bamboo.

All parrot finches have iridescent blue in their plumage, together with some areas of green. Most, but not all of them, also have red in the head, rump or tail regions. They have characteristically high-pitched voices; the song, for instance, is

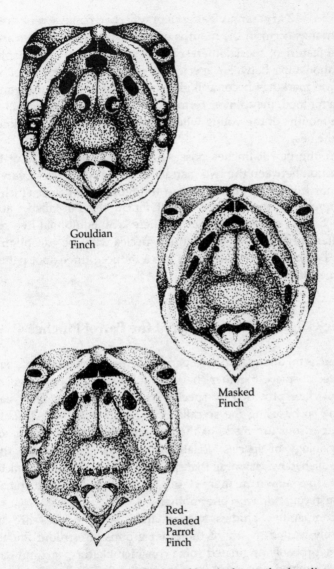

Gouldian
Finch

Masked
Finch

Red-
headed
Parrot
Finch

*Fig. 2 Reflective papillae and throat markings in the mouths of nestlings
of three finches. The reflective papillae, which are at the junction between
the mandibles of the Gouldian Finch and Red-headed Parrot Finch, are
absent in the Masked Finch.*

in the 7-12 kHz range. Patterns of reflective papillae and throat markings occur in the mouths of nestlings and have been used as a feature of special interest by taxonomists trying to establish relationships between species of parrot finches (see below). These markings become highly conspicuous when the young beg for food; they almost certainly function in guiding parents to the mouths of the young when they feed them in the darkness of the nest.

Young parrot finches possess four reflective papillae at the junction between the two mandibles of the beak. These vary in colour from deep cobalt blue in the Blue-faced Parrot Finch to turquoise in the Bamboo Parrot Finch, the Pin-tailed Parrot Finch and Peale's Parrot Finch. There is an additional five-spot pattern of throat markings in all species with the exception of the Bamboo Parrot Finch; this has a reduced three-spot pattern of markings.

The Origin and Evolution of the Parrot Finches

There is no fossil record of a parrot finch, so biologists have been forced to piece together the way in which they have evolved from clues provided by species which exist today. They have done so by using the so-called comparative method. Detailed comparisons are made of the anatomy, behaviour, habits and physiology of species. Relationships between them are then established by assuming that species which have many character-istics in common are more closely related than those which have little in common with one another.

Comparative studies suggest that parrot finches are not closely related to any of the other groups of estrildid finches. They probably originated some considerable time ago and have since evolved separately from the rest of the family. The closest living relative of the parrot finches is evidently the Gouldian Finch. Mitchell (1958) drew attention to several similarities in coloration and habits between the parrot finches and the

Gouldian Finch, and also to striking similarities in the patterns of reflective papillae and throat markings in the nestlings. He noted in particular that the Gouldian Finch is the only estrildid finch which shares the parrot finches' pattern of four papillae and five throat markings (Fig. 2).

Mitchell believed that the Gouldian Finch was, in fact, a parrot finch and should therefore be included in the genus *Erythrura*. The Royal Australian Ornithologists' Union has adopted this convention, but other authorities believe that the relationship is more distant. Guttinger in Ziswiler et al. (1972), for instance, points out that there are several differences between the courtship displays and songs of the Gouldian Finch and parrot finches. He agrees with the more widely accepted view that the Gouldian Finch should be separated from the parrot finches and included in the genus *Chloebia*, of which it is the only species.

However distant or close this relationship may be, it does seem likely that the parrot finches originated in northern Australia, where the Gouldian Finch now lives. Their early ancestors presumably emigrated from there to nearby islands, such as New Guinea or Timor, and then radiated out from this distribution centre to occupy the current range of the group.

The ancestral parrot finches underwent considerable speciation (i.e. have formed new species) as they spread across the Indo-Pacific region and invaded new Pacific islands. Many species must have evolved and become extinct during that process, so that today's tally of 11 species and 24 sub-species is probably only a fraction of the total number which existed in the past. The process of speciation usually occurs when populations of a particular species become sub-divided and geographically isolated from one another. Each population gradually diverges from the others until eventually the differences between them are so great that members of the separated populations would not inter-breed if the chance arose. At this stage they are regarded as separate species. Sub-species represent intermediate stages in the process; members of sub-populations can still inter-breed.

15

Sub-species of the Blue-faced Parrot Finch, for example, are geographically separated and have diverged from one another in coloration and other characteristics (see Chapter 10), but they will still breed with one another if brought together in captivity.

The separation and isolation of populations of parrot finches from one another has probably occurred for many reasons. Islands in the Pacific, for instance, were probably invaded when birds lost their way over the sea or were blown off course during bad weather. The geological separation of land masses has probably been important in isolating populations on some of the larger land masses. Thus, Ziswiler et al. (1972) have suggested that the isolation of the sub-species of the Pin-tailed Parrot Finch occurred as a result of the post-glacial separation of Java from Borneo. Furthermore, the separation and sub-speciation of populations of the Bamboo Parrot Finch may have been caused by changes in sea level which have resulted in the repeated creation and loss of islands along the Malaysian/Indonesian archipelago.

The evolution of the parrot finches and their spread across the Indo-Pacific region and Pacific islands has undoubtedly been complex. Ziswiler et al. (1972) believe, on the basis of exhaustive comparative studies, that they can recognize five groups of closely related species, each of which represents a separate line of evolution and radiation. They give each group the status of sub-genus as follows:

Sub-genus: *Acalanthe*
  Species: Red-headed Parrot Finch
            Peale's Parrot Finch
            Royal Parrot Finch

These species have become specialist feeders on herb or fig seeds. They have developed the novel technique of dehusking seeds by slicing them open with their beaks. The Red-headed Parrot Finch is believed to be the most primitive member of the sub-genus. Its ancestors evidently emigrated from the distribution centre north of Australia to New Caledonia, where the species now exists. Subsequently, birds have found their way to Fiji and then Samoa, and have given rise to Peale's Parrot Finch and the Royal Parrot Finch, respectively. The latter species has subsequently invaded Vanuatu (formerly New Hebrides).

Sub-genus: *Trichroa*
  Species: Blue-faced Parrot Finch
            Katanglad Parrot Finch
            Papuan Parrot Finch

Members of the sub-genus have retained the primitive parrot finch habit of feeding on grass seeds, which they dehusk by crushing between their mandibles. The group has apparently progressed in several directions from the original distribution centre. The Papuan Parrot Finch inhabits New Guinea at, or close to, the distribution centre, but a north-westerly emigration is evident from the occurrence of the Katanglad Parrot Finch in the Philippines. The Blue-faced Parrot Finch has emigrated from the distribution centre to a number of islands adjacent to New Guinea, including Vanuatu.

Sub-genus: *Erythrura*
  Species: Pin-tailed Parrot Finch
            Manila Parrot Finch
            Tri-coloured Parrot Finch

Members of this group have simple (believed to be primitive) courtship displays (see Chapter 3) and are basically grass-seed eaters. They crush seeds in order to dehusk them. The group has evidently progressed through the Sunda Islands, Malaysia, Thailand and western Laos, where the Pin-tailed Parrot Finch exists.

Sub-genus: *Reichenowia*
  Species: Bamboo Parrot Finch

The single species in this sub-genus has undergone considerable sub-speciation. All sub-species are specialist feeders of bamboo seeds. Their emigration route has been in a predominantly north-westerly direction, but over a wide area, including Malaysia, Borneo, Sumatra and Java. -

Sub-genus: *Rhamphostruthus*
Species: Pink-billed Parrot Finch

There is little information on this species but its black head plate and pink beak distinguish it from other parrot finches. Ziswiler et al. (1972) believe that it is distantly related to other members of the group and suggest that it reached Fiji directly, either from Australia or New Guinea.

2
Natural History of Tropical Islands

It is difficult to make generalizations about a geographic area which is as large as that occupied by the parrot finches. Nevertheless, one glance at a map of the region reveals important features (see Fig. 1). First, the area is within 20 degrees of the equator, so it is warm. Secondly, it is dominated by the seas. The relatively small area occupied by land consists principally of a series of large islands such as Sumatra, Borneo, Java and New Guinea, forming the Indo-Pacific region, and innumerable small ones in the Pacific Ocean. The parrot finches are therefore predominantly island birds and, with the exceptions of one sub-species of the Blue-faced Parrot Finch which inhabits northern Australia, one Bamboo Parrot Finch which occurs in Malaysia, and one Pin-tailed Parrot Finch which lives in Malaysia, Thailand and western Laos, they have not invaded the continental land masses.

The large area of sea influences the climate of the region. The air becomes laden with moisture as the winds blow across it and the air is therefore damp. Rainfall is high, probably higher than in any equivalent part of the world. Most weather stations record in excess of 200-250 cm (79-98 in) of rain per year.

Plant and Animal Life

These warm and humid conditions support a luxuriant vegetation. Much of the region either is, or once was, covered by

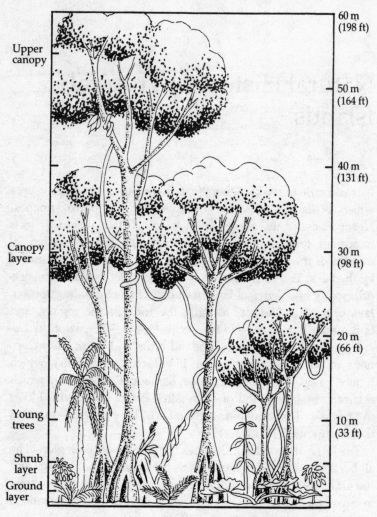

Upper canopy

Canopy layer

Young trees

Shrub layer

Ground layer

60 m (198 ft)

50 m (164 ft)

40 m (131 ft)

30 m (98 ft)

20 m (66 ft)

10 m (33 ft)

Fig. 3 Layering of trees and shrubs in the tropical rain forest.

tropical rain forest. Such forests are characterized by an astonishingly rich flora. Indonesia alone has some 30,000 species of forest trees, shrubs and grasses; 3,000 of these are large trees. While temperate forests are often dominated by one or a few tree types (e.g. the typical oakwood), rain forests are mixed, without stands of any particular tree. Different species occur side by side, providing a seemingly endless variety of shape, colour and form, and giving the impression of utter confusion. Some sense of order is brought about by vertical stratification but even this can be erratic and indistinct. The largest trees, which may reach up to 70 m (229 ft), form an upper canopy. Below this there are usually two or more tiers of shorter trees and shrubs. Little light reaches the ground and there is only a sparse growth of grass and shade-loving plants. The nature of the forest changes with altitude as it progresses up mountain slopes. The luxuriant lowland forest gives way to upland forest above about 1,500 m (4,900 ft), where deciduous and coniferous trees become dominant. Thick growths of moss often cover the ground and hang from branches of trees; epiphytes, orchids and ferns also abound at these high altitudes.

Animal life is as rich and diverse as the flora, particularly in the lowland rain forests themselves. Mammals are well represented by primates, including gibbons, macaques, leaf monkeys, orang-utans and langurs. Birds are plentiful, often occurring in large mixed-species flocks which forage noisily through the vegetation, each species with its own specialized method of feeding. Amphibians are well adapted to the damp conditions and many tree frogs exploit temporary rain-water pools as places in which to lay their eggs. There is an immense invertebrate life, including huge millipedes, centipedes and butterflies.

Finding a Place to Live

Living organisms compete fiercely with one another for places to live, and normally only those that are highly adapted to particular habitats are able to survive in them. A problem facing parrot finches is that the typical estrildid grassland habitat is limited in the region, and that which does exist is usually occupied by several species of very successful mannikins (*Lonchura spp.*). Parrot finches cannot compete with them in grassland and have therefore been forced to live in, or close to, the forest. Their transition to forest life is, however, incomplete; most parrot finches live on the edges of forests or in forest clearings. Even the Pink-billed Parrot Finch, which has some-times been described as a true forest-dweller, may venture away from them (see Chapter 16). Nevertheless, the diets of most parrot finches have become adapted to seeds, such as those of fig, bamboo and herbaceous plants, which are readily available in the rain forest. The change in diet has also led to the development of specialist methods of feeding and adaptations of the bill (see Chapter 3).

Competition for living space can be particularly intense between closely related species and different parrot finches would certainly compete with one another if they occurred in the same environment. It is a general rule in ecology, however, that closely related species, which exploit the same limited resources such as food or places to nest, cannot exist together in the same habitat. If they did so, they would compete with one another until one species ousted its rival. Parrot finches tend to avoid competition because each species occurs in a discrete geographic range with little or no overlap with other species. Where overlaps do occur, such as in the case of the Blue-faced Parrot Finch and the Papuan Parrot Finch in New Guinea, the two species avoid one another by living at different altitudes. The Papuan Parrot Finch inhabits areas which are between 1,000 and 2,000 m (3,280-6,560 ft) above sea level, while the Blue-faced Parrot Finch lives above 2,000 m. Meetings between members of the two species are presumably infrequent. Various sub-species of the Bamboo Parrot Finch escape competition with other parrot finches in the same way. They forage relatively low down on mountain slopes on islands which they have to themselves, but are forced by competition to live at higher levels on islands where there are other species of parrot finches.

Table 2 The effects of competition from other species of parrot finches on the habitat (altitudes) occupied by Bamboo Parrot Finches on different islands. (Based on data from Ziswiler et al., 1972)

Island	Parrot Finch living on same island	Highest altitude of competing species m (ft)	Lowest altitude occupied by Bamboo Parrot Finch m (ft)
Mindoro	none	–	1,200 (3,940)
Lombok	none	–	300 (980)
Flores	none	–	700 (2,300)
Sumbawa	none	–	300 (980)
		Ave:	625 (2,050)
Luzon	Manila	1,000 (3,280)	1,600 (5,250)
Mindanao	Katanglad	1,500 (4,920)	2,000 (6,560)
Borneo	Pin-tailed	1,400 (4,590)	1,500 (4,920)
Malaysia	Pin-tailed	1,000 (3,280)	1,100 (3,610)
Java	Pin-tailed	1,000 (3,280)	1,600 (5,250)
Celebes	Blue-faced	1,500 (4,920)	1,800 (5,905)
	Ave:	1,233 (4,045)	Ave: 1,600 (5,250)

Habitat Destruction and Island Birds

The parrot finches' struggle for existence in the wild is intense enough but it is made immeasurably worse by human interference with the natural environment. The rain forests have been one of the prime targets for destruction and are now seriously over-exploited. This has not always been the case. At one time, local human populations lived in harmony with the rain forest, collecting its abundant resources, such as gum, resin, fruit, edible plants and game, without inflicting long-term damage. Nowadays, the forests are rich sources of timber and are also being cleared by burning so that the land can be used for cattle farming. This is basically for the production of beef which is needed to satisfy the demand for hamburgers in the western world, especially the United States and Europe. The rate of destruction is almost unbelievable. It has been estimated that, worldwide, an area of forest equivalent to the size of Switzerland is being destroyed each year.

Habitat deterioration is also a problem in places where the forest still exists. Again, human activities are to blame. Introduced passion-fruit plants, for instance, have blanketed huge areas of native forests in Hawaii. Similarly, guava is rapidly becoming the dominant member of what remains of forests on Mauritius. Introduced animals can be equally damaging. Rabbits, sheep and goats seriously over-graze some areas, while rats and populations of feral cats can become dangerous predators of native animals, which may lack appropriate escape responses or other effective means of combating them.

A particular problem facing an island population is that, simply by virtue of the area available to it, it is small. Any. sudden catastrophe can therefore have disastrous results, either by knocking out the population altogether or by reducing its numbers to such a low level that it cannot recover. Species on large land masses are cushioned from these effects. Here catastrophes usually leave 'pockets' of species unharmed in sufficiently large numbers to breed successfully and replenish the population again. The seriousness of this problem is underlined by King (1985) who has estimated that 93 per cent of the 93 species and 83 sub-species of birds which have become extinct since 1600 have been the inhabitants of islands. The Pacific has been hit particularly hard; in modern times the large majority of extinctions are occurring there. Some Pacific islands are already in desperate straits. The island of Hawaii, for instance, has lost 24 bird species from its fauna and 29 (62 per cent) of those that remain are classified as endangered.

The island habit of the parrot finches, coupled with the destruction and deterioration of natural habitats, means that they are a vulnerable group. Already the future of some of them is in doubt. The Pink-billed Parrot Finch is probably most at risk. It is restricted to the rain forests of Viti Levu on Fiji, but these have now largely been cleared. The little forest that remains is under threat of being destroyed and replaced with plantations of Australian conifers. Ziswiler et al. (1972) estimated that, at the time of their survey, there were no more than 300-400 of the species remaining. One sub-species of the Royal Parrot Finch (*E. cyaneovirens serena*), on Aneiteum Island, may already be a victim of habitat destruction and another sub-species (*E. cyaneovirens cyaneovirens*), on Vanuatu, may also be endangered. In this latter case, the sub-species is threatened by fierce competition from other fig-eating birds.

Competition from waxbills, which were brought to islands as cage birds, and then released or escaped to establish themselves in the wild, also pose threats to parrot finches in some Pacific islands. Introduced mannikins and red-eared waxbills compete with the Blue-faced Parrot Finch on Vanuatu, and with the Red-headed Parrot Finch on New Caledonia. Similarly, Peale's Parrot Finch faces competition from red Avadavats and spice finches on Fiji.

The versatility and ability of some parrot finches to adapt to changing environments does, nevertheless, give cause for optimism. The Pin-tailed Parrot Finch has exploited the man-made habitat provided by rice fields. It is so successful that it has become a pest in some parts of its range. Similarly, Peale's Parrot Finch has survived, despite habitat destruction, by switching to a diet in which rice is a major component, and the Samoan sub-species of the Royal Parrot Finch has successfully adapted its diet to seeds of (mostly introduced) herbaceous plants. There is also good news of the Palau sub-species of the Blue-faced Parrot Finch. It was once categorized as endangered, but a survey in 1977-79 showed that it was at least holding its own (Pratt et al., 1980). It survives in moderate numbers on small limestone islands off southern Palau, and is not now believed to be under immediate threat of extinction.

3
Habits

There have been few studies of parrot finches in their natural haunts. A number of ornithologists have provided field records of their occurrence in various localities, with notes on aspects of their habits and behaviour, but the only detailed research is that of the biologists, Dr V. Ziswiler, Dr H.R. Guttinger and Dr H. Bregulla (1972). Further studies are needed, not only to fill gaps in scientific knowledge, but also for the development of good avicultural practice. Aviculturists who take heed of the conditions under which species live, feed and breed in the wild, are far more likely to be able to cater for their needs in captivity than those who attempt to meet their requirements by trial and error guesswork. Knowledge of the natural habits of captive birds also adds to the enjoyment of keeping them. It draws attention to facets of behaviour, such as courtship displays, calls, songs and feeding skills, which may otherwise go unnoticed.

Food and Feeding Habits

As already mentioned in Chapter 2, parrot finches feed from plants which occur in rain forests and several species, though not all, have abandoned the typical estrildid finch diet of grass seeds. Different feeding techniques are needed to cope with these changes in diet and Ziswiler et al. (1972) divided the parrot finches into four groups on the basis of their preferences for different foods and methods of dehusking seeds:

26

Grass Seed Specialists

Pin-tailed Parrot Finch
Manila Parrot Finch
Tri-coloured Parrot Finch
Blue-faced Parrot Finch

These species have retained the typical estrildid finch preference for grass seeds and, in seed selection experiments, they chose these in preference to the seeds of herbaceous plants. They dehusk seeds in the characteristic manner of other members of the Estrildidae. The short beak is used to crush and break the husk. Each seed is positioned between the two mandibles of the beak and then upward pressure from the lower jaw pushes it against a horny pad on the inside of the upper mandible. The crushed husk is discarded and the nutritious seed is swallowed.

Generalists

Red-headed Parrot Finch
Peale's Parrot Finch
Katanglad Parrot Finch

These species include a variety of different seeds in their diets, especially those of herbaceous plants. They have developed a novel method of dehusking seeds. The husks are actually sliced open. Seeds are held between the sharp cutting edges of the lower mandible and the ridges of the upper mandible. The lower jaw is then moved in pronounced backwards and forwards movements, cutting the husk and separating it from the rest of the seed.

Bamboo Specialists

Bamboo Parrot Finch

All of the sub-species of the Bamboo Parrot Finch take seeds from bamboo plants. They forage on small and medium-sized bamboos as well as climbing bamboos which may reach close to the top of the forest canopy. Seeds are dehusked by crushing.

Fig Specialists

Papuan Parrot Finch
Royal Parrot Finch
Pink-billed Parrot Finch

These three species all feed on fig fruits, but employ different techniques from one another in doing so. The Royal Parrot Finch detaches the fruit by biting through its stalk. The fruit is then carried to a perching place. Here the outer covering is ripped off with the protruding hook of the upper mandible. Cutting movements of the lower mandible then tear open the softer inner parts. The seeds are devoured one by one until the fruit is empty, by which time the skin is turned inside out.

The Papuan Parrot Finch tackles fig fruits by pecking holes in them with the sharp tip of its bill. Seeds are then picked out through the hole. Both the Royal Parrot Finch and the Papuan Parrot Finch dehusk seeds by using the cutting technique described above for the generalists.

The way in which the Pink-billed Parrot Finch treats figs depends on their size. Those that are about the size of hazelnuts are torn open and the pulp of the fruit and the seeds are devoured. The skins of these fruits, like those eaten by Royal Parrot Finches, are turned inside out. Smaller, pea-sized fruits are taken into the beak, squashed and swallowed whole.

Breeding Behaviour

Little is known about the breeding behaviour of parrot finches in the wild and the only detailed information available is from Guttinger's studies of captive finches (described in Ziswiler et al., 1972).

Courtship is an early sign that birds are coming into breeding condition. Males give complex displays to their mates. On the basis of these displays, they can be divided into two groups:

Group One

Males of the Bamboo Parrot Finch, Pin-tailed Parrot Finch, Tri-coloured Parrot Finch and Manila Parrot Finch gather a small bundle of nesting material in the beak before displaying. The male then flies to the female. He starts to sing a soft warbling song in front of her, which is inaudible from more than a few metres away. Simultaneously, he commences a courtship dance in which his head is held horizontally and turned jerkily from side to side. The male then bows, lowering his head so that the beak comes almost into contact with the feet. Finally, he jumps closer to the female, jerking his head upwards and, at the same time, lifting his tail and moving it from side to side. A receptive female reacts by moving her head and tail synchronously with the male. She may also bow simultaneously with him. A pair usually repeats these displays several times. Copulation has not been observed and possibly occurs in the nest.

Group Two

Courtship of the remaining parrot finches is initially similar to that described above. They start by performing the same display but then go on to a second display, which is initiated by the female flying away from the male. She alights at a suitable perching place and performs a characteristic display which resembles the begging posture of a young bird; she crouches and turns her head sideways and upwards. The female then flies off with the male in pursuit, both birds singing the nest invitation call. Copulation may follow a series of short flights. The female perches stiffly and assumes a stooped posture; she is mounted by the male, which grasps her head feathers in his beak and copulates with her.

Courtship Songs

Parrot finch courtship songs are shrill and are restricted to narrow frequency ranges. Some species have highly repetitive songs. The Tri-coloured Parrot Finch, for instance, has only six basic elements in its song and these are uttered repeatedly.

Nesting

Once pair bonds have been formed, birds search for suitable nest sites. A bird which finds a site attracts its mate to it by making chattering nest invitation calls. The two birds then perform a mutual display at the site, raising their heads upwards and making nibbling movements of the beak.

In probably all species the male collects nesting materials while his mate remains at the nesting site, building the nest. There is little defence of the area adjacent to the nest; other members of the species are allowed to build in close proximity. The clutch size varies from species to species, but eggs hatch after 12-14 days' incubation. Young are reared by both parents. There is no nest hygiene in most species (but see Chapter 10), except that after the fourteenth day the young position themselves so that the droppings fall on the outer edge of the nest. Nestlings solicit food from their parents with a high-pitched 'zi-zi-zi' call. Fledging occurs between 21 and 26 days after hatching. Young remain with the parents, which rely on a 'zuuu' sounding location call to keep in contact with them.

In most species the pair bond lasts for one season only. Members of pairs split up after breeding and re-pair, evidently with new partners, the following season.

Social Behaviour

Most of the parrot finches occur in flocks or family groups in the wild. The Pink-billed Parrot Finch is perhaps the most solitary, but even it is sometimes seen in groups. Calls are important as a means of communication in social interactions. The following are made by parrot finches:

Nest begging call:	high pitched 'zi-zi-zi'.
Location call:	given by newly fledged birds. It sounds like a lengthened 'zuuu'. Parents use it to locate their offspring.
Contact call:	a high-pitched call described as 'zit-zit'. The frequency range of 7.5-11 kHz is exceptionally high.
Nest invitation call:	similar to a begging call. It is given on discovery of a suitable nest site.
Fear call:	young parrot finches give a 'zieg-zieg' call when handled. The female makes a similar call during copulation.
Warning call:	long sequence of high-pitched calls.
Rage call:	given when one bird threatens another. In some species it sounds like 'tege-tete-tege'; in others, 'derrr'.
Distance trill:	uttered by both sexes during the pursuit flight in courtship. A series of calls which sound like a metallic 'tirrr'.

4

The Bird Trade
and the Future of Aviculture

The Estrildidae, the family of birds to which the parrot finches belong, is deservedly popular among aviculturists. The attractive coloration and engaging personalities of its members recommend them as cage birds. They also have relatively modest requirements in captivity and many of them can be bred successfully without excessive demands on the time and energy of their owners. Domestic strains of several species, especially those which originate from Australia, such as the Gouldian Finch, the Long-tailed Grassfinch, the Masked Finch and the Zebra Finch, are now available throughout the world.

Unfortunately, only two of the parrot finches can be regarded as sufficiently well established in captivity to fall into this category. These are the Red-headed Parrot Finch and the Blue-faced Parrot Finch. There is, however, an urgent need to develop husbandry methods for other species, especially those which face an uncertain future in the wild because of the destruction of their natural habitats. Sadly, programmes to conserve the natural environment cannot be relied upon to save them. Massive pressure for economic development eats up the rain forest at an alarming rate and only those conservation programmes which have the highest priority are likely to be successful.

The problem of conservation is one to which aviculturists, especially amateur hobbyists, can make an enormous contribution. They undoubtedly have the skills to establish self-maintaining stocks of many species in captivity, including most, if not all, of the parrot finches. Unfortunately, two major barriers stand in the way of such developments in aviculture. The first relates to difficulties in obtaining birds. Wild-trapped parrot finches, especially species such as the Royal Parrot Finch, the Manila Parrot Finch, and the Pink-billed Parrot Finch, rarely, if ever, appear in dealers' lists. As pressure increases to control the international trade in wild-trapped birds, it is extremely doubtful that they will be available from dealers in the future.

The second barrier concerns the ways in which species undergo change in captivity; birds which become established in aviculture become less and less like their wild relatives. Varieties of the domestic canary have, for example, undergone remarkable changes in shape, coloration, song and behaviour. Some of them are so bizarre, as seen through the eyes of a conservationist, that they can only be regarded as curiosities and would stand no chance at all of surviving if they were reintroduced to the wild.

International Trade in Wild-trapped Birds

Aviculturists are understandably reluctant to criticize the international bird trade because it is their only source of species which are not bred in captivity. Moves to curtail or control it more effectively are viewed with apprehension because they restrict the numbers and varieties of foreign species which are available to the hobby. The view is, however, short-sighted. Our failure to speak out against the many unsavoury aspects of the trade is interpreted as indifference and does little either to raise our status with the general public or encourage legislators to arrive at regulations which will protect the interests of genuine aviculturists. It is surely time that aviculturists worked together with government bodies, environmental agencies and all those who have the welfare of birds at heart, to prohibit unacceptable trading practices. Little, if any, defence can be offered against the following:

The Trade in Endangered Species

Aviculture cannot make serious claims to contribute to species conservation while it fails to speak out against, and still provides the outlet for, illegally trapped birds. Such activities are almost impossible to police effectively in developing countries, and cases of bird smuggling are reported with alarming frequency (see, e.g. Nilsson, 1981).

Cruelty to Trapped Birds

Consignments of wild-trapped birds sometimes suffer levels of mortality which are totally unacceptable. Carter & Currey (1987) estimate that 50 per cent of the 20 million birds which are trapped annually in the Senegal for the bird trade, die before exportation from that country. The major causes of death appear to be stress, lack of ventilation in carrying boxes, high temperatures, overcrowding, lack of suitable food or drinking facilities and disease.

Tragically, this is far from the end of the story. A further 20 per cent of the original survivors die either during export or at quarantine stations in the countries receiving them. Even then birds get into the wrong hands and it is estimated that probably less than 10 per cent of the wild-trapped 'foreign' birds which are released on to the market in the United Kingdom, survive their first year of caged life. If this pattern is repeated in other countries, it means that only 4.2 per cent of wild-trapped birds live for longer than a year in captivity.

Disease

Cage birds can be carriers of commercially important diseases of poultry, especially Newcastle disease (see, e.g. Nilsson, 1981), and other diseases which can affect humans, particularly psittacosis.

These malpractices must be eradicated, and aviculturists will only gain the credibility they deserve when they are seen to work towards this end. There are, of course, many honest and reputable traders who want to protect their livelihoods. There is no reason why they should not do so. A properly managed bird trade could function without damaging wild populations of birds and without causing unnecessary cruelty to trapped birds, but to do so, it will need much tighter control than that which now exists.

The prospects for the future will surely become brighter once a responsible stance has been taken concerning the trade. It is difficult to imagine that licences to trap and import birds will be denied to groups which can demonstrate genuine intentions to set up breeding programmes for their conservation. Indeed such licences are already granted. Specialist bodies, such as the Wildfowl Trust, the World Pheasant Association and the Crane Foundation, as well as zoos and some universities, receive favourable treatment. They have received consignments of species whose existence is threatened and, in some cases, have made significant contributions to conservation. For instance, the efforts of the Wildfowl Trust have saved the Hawaiian Goose from the very brink of extinction (see, e.g. Kear & Berger, 1980).

Other avicultural groups should also be able to contribute, including those whose interests in keeping birds are primarily as a hobby. Their skills in establishing species in captivity can rival, or even better, those of more 'professional' organizations. The most striking successes of amateur hobbyists followed the Australian Government's ban on the export and import of all wildlife in 1960. The ban has remained in force and currently comes under the Wildlife Protection (Regulations of Exports and Imports) Act. It put a sudden, and (apart from occasional reports of smuggling) total stop to the world trade in wild-trapped Australian birds. Despite this, aviculturists were remarkably successful in breeding up stocks from the birds which were already in captivity at the time of the ban. For example, European and American aviculturists have established almost all of the native estrildid finches in captivity. Several, such as the Gouldian Finch and the Zebra Finch, are now thoroughly domesticated and most are still available outside Australia. According to the Australian Finch Society's 1987/88 *Handbook*, 15 out of the 18 species can still be obtained in Britain. Similar successes occurred with Australian parrots. The large majority of them were established and have been maintained in captivity throughout the world.

The achievements of Australian aviculturists are no less praiseworthy. They were deprived of formerly imported 'foreign' species by their government's ban but they, too, established stocks of many of them. The Avicultural Society of Australia's *Bird Price Guide 1986* included the following 'foreign' parrots, all of which are now bred in Australia: the Madagascar Lovebird (*Agapornis cana*), Fisher's Lovebird (*A. fischeri*), Nyasa Lovebird (*A. lilianae*), Masked Lovebird (*A. personata*), Peach-faced Lovebird (*A. roseicollis*), Jendaya Conure (*Aratinga jendaya*), Yellow-fronted Kariki (*Cyanoramphus auriceps*), Red-fronted Kariki (*C. novaezelandiae*), Nanday Conure (*Nandayus nenday*), Plum-headed Parrot (*Psittacula cyanocephala*), Ring-necked parakeet (*Psittacula krameri*) and African Grey Parrot (*Psittacus erithacus*).

There were also notable successes with finches: the Queensland Finch Society's *Official Price Guide for 1986* still includes prices for 22 out of the 122 species of estrildid finches which originate from Africa or Asia. Successes with another small finch are also worthy of mention. The Cuban Finch (*Tiaris canova*) is so well established in Australia and is bred in such numbers that surplus birds were exported to the United States in 1982; the Australian Government was prepared to license the export of a non-native species.

Unfortunately, aviculturists have not devoted the same attention to species which are still regularly available as wild-trapped birds. It seems that the continued influx of birds from

Table 3 Comparative prices of estrildid finches in Australia and the United Kingdom. Queensland prices are taken from the Queensland Finch Society's *Official Price Guide for 1986* and UK prices are mean prices from advertisements (first issue of each month) in *Cage and Aviary Birds* in 1986.

Species	(prices in £) Queensland	United Kingdom
Red Avadavat	16.2	9.5 ± 1.4
Green Avadavat	75.6	18.3 ± 1.1
Spice Finch	2.2	6.1 ± 0.9
Black Nun	6.5	7.4 ± 0.9
White Nun	6.5	7.0 ± 1.0
Tricoloured Nun	8.6	9.4 ± 1.5
Rufous-backed Mannikin	19.4	11.0 ± 1.2
Red-headed Parrot Finch	28.1	39.0 ± 6.3
Blue-faced Parrot Finch	10.8	19.8 ± 2.5
Indian Silverbill	43.2	7.0 ± 1.4
African Silverbill	21.6	4.3 ± 0.5
Aurora Finch	6.5	11.5 ± 1.4
Blue-capped Cordon Bleu	41.0	9.8 ± 1.3
Blue-breasted Cordon Bleu	129.5	
Red-cheeked Cordon Bleu	9.7	9.6 ± 1.0
Firefinch	5.4	14.0 ± 5.7
Cutthroat	4.3	4.8 ± 1.1
Lavender Finch	183.5	11.1 ± 1.9
Melba Finch	8.6	20.0 ± 2.7
Orange-breasted Waxbill	7.6	8.1 ± 0.6
Orange-cheeked Waxbill	215.9	5.0 ± 0.6
St Helena Waxbill	9.7	4.8 ± 0.5
Mean Prices	39.1	11.3

the wild actually inhibits the development of methods for their husbandry. It does so because wild-trapped birds are so readily available, and therefore so cheap, that there is little incentive to breed them or establish stocks of them in captivity. The failure to breed Asian and African estrildid finches in Europe and the

United States illustrates this point. Most of them have been, and can be, bred in captivity but only three species are sufficiently well established to be regarded as domesticated. These are the Blue-faced Parrot Finch, the Red-headed Parrot Finch and the Java Sparrow. The situation in Australia, where Asian and African species are no longer imported, is quite different. These birds are prized and serious efforts are made to breed and maintain them.

What Are We Doing to Birds in Captivity?

Husbandry practices will also need to be reviewed if aviculture is to contribute to species conservation. Some practices actually conflict with the aims of conservation. One problem is that aviculturists 'change' species by breeding them to 'recognized' exhibition standards. The result is that domestic varieties of the budgerigar, canary, Zebra Finch, and so on, are very different from wild birds. Coloration is subject to particularly rapid change because the colour mutations that arise from time to time are sought after and used as breeding stock. The consequence is that whereas the wild budgerigar, for example, is basically green in colour, domestic varieties are available in a remarkable range of greys, blues, yellows and greens, as well as albino forms.

The process of keeping birds in confinement in itself also leads to change. Evans & Fidler (1986) found that domestically bred Gouldian Finches tended to be larger and more brightly coloured but less active than wild-trapped ones, and that they had lost at least one call from the natural repertoire of vocalizations.

Some such effects are probably unavoidable, but the same cannot be said for the biologically pointless habit of hybridizing species. It is, unfortunately, widespread. Immelmann (1965), for example, lists known hybrids of 15 out of the 18 Australian estrildids. The products are worthless from the viewpoint of conservation and can soon lead to loss of species identity.

Interbreeding of different species of captive Cordon Bleus in Australia has, for instance, been so rife that almost all of the few remaining Blue-capped Cordon Bleus there are said to carry some characteristics of either the Red-cheeked Cordon Bleu or the Blue-breasted Cordon Bleu. Unfortunately, some European breeders have hybridized parrot finches, notably the Katanglad Parrot Finch, even before it has been fully established in captivity (see Chapter 12).

5

Housing, Breeding and Feeding Requirements in Captivity

The further development of husbandry techniques for parrot finches presents both an exciting and a daunting challenge for aviculturists. As we have seen in previous chapters, several species are endangered in the wild and their only hope of long-term survival may be in captivity. Every effort must be made to ensure that as many species as possible are established and maintained as cage birds.

Unfortunately, opportunities have sometimes been wasted in the past. It is frustrating, for example, that the Royal Parrot Finch has been kept and bred in captivity (see Chapter 14) but not established. As far as is known, it is now never imported and there is no guarantee, therefore, that the chance to breed it in aviculture will ever occur again. If it does, we must be ready to make full use of it. The same is true of the Manila Parrot Finch (see Chapter 8). It has been imported into Europe on several occasions, but has yet to be bred in captivity. At least in part this is because aviculturists fail to give it full attention when it has been available.

This chapter gives a general account of the husbandry of parrot finches. Techniques for two species, the Blue-faced Parrot Finch and the Red-headed Parrot Finch, are highly successful, but there is still much to learn about the others. We hope that the recommendations included here can be used as a basis for the development of more refined methods. What is known of the specific requirements of individual species is included in the following chapters, which deal with each in turn.

Caring for Chinese

box (on the floor), in which to build a nest, this is by no means guaranteed. Because they have usually been artificially produced for many generations, the instinct to brood and rear is often much reduced. In this case you will have to resort to an incubator.

Unfortunately, if you decide that you definitely want to try artificial incubation, incubators are not cheap. I would recommend a forced air machine (ie one with fan-assisted air movement) that must have an electronic thermostat. I would further suggest that £50 represents a minimum for a reasonable machine.

Eggs should be set in batches of five — 10 at a time and should not be more than approximately 10 days old. Follow the instructions accompanying the incubator — the manufacturer knows best! The incubation period is 16 days.

Painted Quail

by Carl Garnham

CHINESE Painted Quail are a fully domesticated species, like Canaries and Budgerigars, having been captive-bred for a great many generations indeed. Like all species of Quail, CPQ require a diet of 50 per cent seed and 50 per cent poultry chick crumbs. The seed can be any small seed, mix or plain millet. If they are in an aviary with Finches, the seed will be from spillages. Supply only chick crumbs on the floor specifically for Quail. The best way to offer the crumbs is probably in a large dog bowl or something similar, so as to avoid waste.

The high protein content of the crumbs will ensure that CPQ are likely to produce good numbers of fertile, viable eggs — something a diet of seed only cannot do.

Although many CPQ will go broody if provided with some form of cover, or a small nest-

hanging 4-6in above the floor of the brooder. This can be gradually raised until they are hardened off. For the first couple of days the chicks should be restricted to an area of around one square foot beneath the bulb to let them know where to return to later. Floor covering is ideally a kitchen towel or corrugated paper (not card).

To start them feeding, sieve some chick crumbs in an ordinary kitchen flour sieve. The fine grains which fall through are ideal — lightly scatter them directly on the floor of the brooder. Drinking water is the only other thing required and is best offered in a dipper-type fountain placed directly on the floor.

The Birdroom

Parrot finches are adapted to survive in a natural world which is very different from that available in even the most lavish of birdrooms. While it would be impossible to simulate wild conditions accurately in captivity, close attention should, however, be paid to them. The provision of adequate light, temperature and humidity are particularly important.

Sufficient window space is desirable to provide good natural light in the birdroom, although not to such an extent that the room suffers from over-heating in summer or becomes too cold in winter. Controlled artificial light is almost always needed in order to supplement light intensity and to extend day-length in winter. Daylight lasts for about 12 hours per day near the equator but many aviculturists artificially increase the light regime to about 14 or 15 hours per day in the birdroom. Although this seems generous, it is evidently to the liking of the birds subjected to it.

Some form of heating is also required in cold climates. Several parrot finches occur at relatively high altitudes on mountain slopes and are therefore presumably exposed to low temperatures. They are, nevertheless, still birds of the tropics or subtropics, and survival in prolonged cold and damp conditions, like those experienced for much of the year in Britain, is too demanding for such tiny creatures. They lose heat rapidly and, even if they do survive, will have to expend a considerable amount of energy simply in keeping the body warm. Their health and breeding success is bound to suffer in the long term. The lowest recommended temperature for parrot finches is between about 17 and 21° C (63-70° F).

Humidity is not a problem in most birdrooms, but it should not be ignored, especially if electric heating, which dries the air, is used. Eggs lose water by evaporation. If the relative humidity drops below 45 per cent they become dehydrated, so that the embryos in them die (so-called 'dead in shell'). The provision of ample bathing water for the birds and/or potted plants in the birdroom may dampen the air sufficiently to rectify the fault if it does occur. In extreme cases, the installation of a humidifier may be necessary.

Over all, considerable attention should be given to cleanliness in the birdroom. The floor should be easy to clean and kept free of debris around which dirt can accumulate. Concrete floors are ideal since they can be washed and scrubbed, and they have the added bonus of being vermin-proof. Cages should be washed and disinfected periodically and perches given an occasional wipe with a cloth soaked in a disinfectant.

Cages

Cages for parrot finches should be at least 1 m (long) × 50 × 50 cm (39 × 20 × 20 in) in size. Smaller cages give birds insufficient room for exercise so that they become obese, with disastrous effects on their breeding performance. The box type of cage with solid sides, back, floor and roof, and a standard 'foreign finch' front, is ideal. Plastic-coated chipboard is an excellent construction material. All-wire cages are less suitable for breeding as they give parrot finches insufficient security and birds in them can suffer from stress. A removable metal or wooden tray, preferably covered with newspaper over which coarse sand and grit are scattered, eases the problem of keeping the cage floor clean. Perches of about 1 cm (0.39 in) in diameter, which 'twist' into cage fronts and are attached only to them, are a good investment. Their surface should be roughened so that the birds do not have problems in gripping them.

Cage Utensils

Recommended cage utensils are as follows:

Water Fonts
It is essential that the birds' water supply is clean. Water which has been fouled by droppings can lead to intestinal problems,

especially diarrhoea. This is probably the single greatest cause of death in cage birds. Standard water fountains which clip onto cage fronts are good, as long as the water in them is changed at least every other day.

Seed Containers

Large shallow dishes, or seed hoppers which have drawers for catching husks, are probably the most suitable seed containers because parrot finches are inveterate seed scatterers.

Soft Food Feeders

The finger drawers, which are used by canary breeders and which slot into cage fronts, are excellent containers.

Cuttlefish Bone Clips

Pieces of cuttlefish bone should be clipped onto cage fronts, preventing the inevitable contamination which occurs if they are placed on the cage floor.

Baths

Baths which fit onto cage fronts should also be provided, and birds should be given the opportunity to bathe very frequently to maintain feather condition. Since birds will also drink their bathing water, it must be kept clean.

Aviaries

Aviculturists whose primary aim is to breed finches as prolifically as possible, usually prefer to keep their stock in cages, at least during the breeding season. They then have full control over them, can decide who mates with whom, can make regular nest-box inspections without disrupting the entire collection, and so on. Colony breeding in planted aviaries is less desirable from this point of view because it is, to a large extent, a matter of letting the birds get on with things for themselves.

There are, of course, compromises between the use of cages and aviaries. Many aviculturists allow their birds to fly in outside flights during the non-breeding season but bring them back into the birdroom to breed. Others give the birds access to outside flights while breeding by constructing small flights, perhaps 2 m (long) × 2 m (high) × 50 cm (wide) (78 × 78 × 20 in), attached to the birdroom. Cages inside the birdroom lead into the flights, and generally one pair has a cage/flight to itself. Plants are normally excluded from such flights. Their floors are covered with coarse sand, which can be raked over from time to time and replaced between seasons.

There is more to aviculture, however, than simply breeding as many birds as possible. For those whose interest is in the aesthetic value of their collection, there is no better opportunity of watching them and appreciating their beauty, than in a large well-planted aviary. Parrot finches are good aviary subjects. They are colourful and active, and also stand up well to the turmoil of mixed collections. They are unaggressive towards other species, but are sturdy enough to look after themselves. Breeding should not be discounted in any case, even if it is less efficient than in cages. Some species are prolific in outside flights, and it may turn out that one or more of those parrot finches which have yet to be bred in captivity, will only rear young successfully in the seclusion of well-planted quarters. Care must be taken if several species of parrot finch are housed in the same aviary. There is then a danger of hybridization which is undesirable (see Chapter 4).

The standard aviary has an enclosed shelter with an attached flight which has an open (i.e. wire netting) roof and open sides. It has the advantage that, being unprotected from the weather, plants inside it grow easily with little attention. Unfortunately, any other inmates of the flight are also exposed to the weather and, in all but the warmest climates, small birds, such as finches, will require protection. This can be provided in the more enclosed box aviary, which has a covered roof and is covered on three sides. Since it is open on one side only, careful siting will lead to almost total protection from winds. The problem then becomes one of providing sufficient water and light to support plant growth. Regular watering is necessary and it may be desirable to install an automatic watering and/or spraying device. The light requirement can be met by using a translucent plastic material for the aviary's roof. There are many possibilities which incorporate features of both standard and box aviaries. It is, for example, possible to have part of the roof open so that some rainwater and direct sunlight reaches the plants and birds inside the aviary.

The materials used for aviary construction will depend on local availability, personal choice and budget. Wood is attractive, but in countries where there is a threat of termites, alternatives are desirable. Tubular metal poles, corrugated iron, cement sheets and plastic sheets may well have their place, as well as bricks, mortar and breeze blocks. Polystyrene and glass fibre are useful insulating materials where they are needed. Wire netting should be about 1 cm (0.39 in) mesh for birds as small as parrot finches.

The aviary shelter should be provided with the usual services. An electricity supply is essential for providing supplementary light in winter and, if necessary, heat. A water supply is also desirable and, if possible, it should also be available in the outside flight. A slow trickle of water into a suitable container ensures that clean drinking water is always available, and the overflow can be used to irrigate the plants. If food is provided in the outside flight, it can be offered in hoppers or dishes, which are placed in a deep tray suspended from the roof of the aviary.

Vermin must be kept out of the aviary. The house mouse is probably the most frequent pest, but rats which gain access to flights can be more damaging because they will kill the inhabitants, as will snakes in those parts of the world where they are pests. The main problem in preventing entry is at the base of the flight: rodents are capable of burrowing in from outside and they, and snakes, will exploit even the slimmest gaps that exist between building materials. A common way of preventing access is to sink L-shaped pieces of wire-netting or galvanized metal (perhaps 45 × 45 cm/18 × 18 in) into the soil all round the flight and shelter. If attacks from other predators, such as hawks or cats, cause a threat, open wire netting panels may have to be shielded with second panels, forming double-wiring protection; the panels should be about 10cm (4 in) apart.

Providing a Balanced Diet

The foods provided for birds in captivity must satisfy all of their nutrient requirements (i.e. provide balanced diets), as well as being ones which are acceptable to them. It is rarely feasible to give captive species the foods on which they feed in the wild, and in the cases of most parrot finches, this is virtually impossible. The one exception is the Pin-tailed Parrot Finch, which feeds predominantly on rice. Although this food can easily be obtained, it would be unrealistic to attempt to find natural foods for the species that feed on the seeds of rain forest plants, such as figs and bamboos. The problem facing the aviculturist is then one of finding suitable alternatives to natural foods. Fortunately, some species, particularly those whose main food is grass seed, will readily adapt to the usual 'foreign finch mixture' of canary and millet seeds. Other species present greater problems but even the Vanuatuan Royal Parrot Finch, which is a fig-seed eater, has been weaned off this diet and persuaded to take more readily obtainable foods (see Chapter 14).

Care must be taken, however, to ensure that the foods provided do actually give a balanced diet. Signs that something is missing may not be immediately obvious but long-term indications are poor health, lack of vigour and failure to breed. The changes can be dramatic once the defect is remedied and a suitable food supplement is found. The breakthrough in the culture of the Bamboo Parrot Finch, for example, seems to have occurred from the chance discovery that breeding birds require fruit in their diet. The precise nutrient which is provided by this

Table 4 Nutrients in the balanced diet.

Component in the diet	Some natural sources	Possible sources in aviculture
Carbohydrates	grass and other seeds	millets, canary and other seeds
Fats	herb seeds	niger, hemp, maw and rape seeds
Proteins	insects and seeding grasses	soft food; live food; germinating seeds; seeding grasses; hard-boiled egg
Vitamins	green food; fruit; (Vitamin D manufactured by skin in sunlight)	green food; vitamin supplements
Mineral salts	various foods	mineralized grit; mineral supplements; cuttlefish bone (calcium); cattle mineral supplement

food is unknown and it is not certain that fruits (other than figs) are a component of the natural diet. Nevertheless, their provision in captivity appears to be a factor in breeding success (see Chapter 6).

The basic components of the balanced diet in birds are the same as those in our own diet, namely, carbohydrates, fats, proteins, vitamins and mineral salts. They are needed to sustain all bodily processes, such as growth, feather development, muscle action, egg and sperm production, and so on. Nutrient requirements are not always the same, however. There are, for example, three times during a bird's life when it has a particular need for proteins: (i) during the period of active growth as a nestling and juvenile; (ii) while moulting; (iii) while breeding. Birds which are nesting have exceptionally high protein requirements because they must meet both their own needs and those of their young. In the wild, they satisfy these needs while nesting by switching from a non-breeding, carbohydrate-rich diet of dry seeds to a protein-rich diet, often of insects and/or seeding grasses. Captive birds must also satisfy their protein needs when they breed and it is essential, therefore, that suitable foods, such as live food, soaked seed, seeding grasses or soft food (see below) are provided for them to do so.

It is strongly recommended that aviculturists adopt a feeding schedule for their stock, which simulates feeding in the wild. In particular, it is essential that protein/rich foods are available throughout the breeding cycle. The following foods should therefore be provided during the breeding and non-breeding seasons:

Non-breeding Season

Always available:	dry seed mix
	mineralized grit
	cuttlefish bone
Supplied regularly:	vitamin supplement
	green food

Breeding Season

Always available:	dry seed mix
	mineralized grit
	cuttlefish bone
Supplied once or twice daily:	soft food mix
	and/or seeding grasses
	and/or sprouted seed
	and/or live food
Supplied regularly:	vitamin supplement
	green food

Suitable foods are as follows:

Dry Seed Mix

The basic mix consists of: 25 per cent canary seed: 25 per cent white millet; 25 per cent pannicum millet; 25 per cent plate millet. Other seeds can be provided, depending on the requirements of particular species (see chapters on individual species). Spray millet is often an acceptable addition to the diet.

Germinating (sprouted) Seed

Sprouted seed which has started to germinate should be regarded as a different food from dry seed. Chemical changes occur during germination in which proteins are broken down into their constituent parts (amino acids) making them more readily digestible. To all intents and purposes, therefore, germinating seeds are much better sources of proteins, vitamins and minerals than dry seeds. The following system of soaking is recommended:

(i) Some of the dry seed mix is submerged in water in a covered container. It is left in a warm place, such as on the top of a central heating boiler, as seeds germinate rapidly in temperatures between 25 and 30° C (77-85° F).

(ii) After 12 hours, the seed is emptied into a flour sieve and rinsed with fresh water. After allowing to drain, it is then replaced in the container and put back into the warm place and left for a further 36 hours. When small shoots have emerged from the seeds, they are ready to feed to the birds.

Soaked seeds must remain free of bacterial or fungal contamination. The characteristic smell of fermentation is normal and healthy, but if the soaked seed has an unpleasant odour, it should be discarded. It is advisable for the soaked seed to be thoroughly rinsed under running water. The containers in which the soaked seed is given to the birds should also be thoroughly cleaned after each use.

Green Food
Wild plants, such as chickweed, dandelion, clover and seeding grasses, are usually accepted, although birds may be reluctant to sample a new type of green food which they have not previously experienced. Lettuce, chicory, spinach and cress are acceptable garden plants. Whatever its source, green food must be free of contamination from insecticides, fertilizers or other harmful substances. It is wise to wash it before offering it to the birds.

Soft Food Mix
The following mix is recommended: 4 parts of a proprietary brand of canary-rearing food (soft food); 1 part of wheat germ extract (flake); 1/100th part of cattle mineral supplement. The mineral supplement is the same as that added to cattle feed by farmers. The mix is moistened lightly with water. It should become soft and crumbly, but not sticky, when rolled between the thumb and forefinger.

Live Food
Termites, mealworms, whiteworms, ant pupae and flour moth larvae can be offered. Only limited quantities of mealworms should be supplied, however, since they can cause an imbalance of minerals.

Vitamin and Mineral Supplements
There are several good supplements on the market. Most are added to the drinking water or to soft food.

Breeding Birds

Most breeders allow their birds access to large flights when they are not breeding. This gives them maximum opportunity to moult and to recover from the stresses of previous breeding efforts, which may have been a heavy drain on their resources.

The two sexes are caged in separate flights so that existing pair-bonds are certainly broken and, if desired, birds can be re-paired with new mates the following year. The diet is basically an austere one of dry seeds (see above). Protein-rich foods, such as soft food, are not given as additional items until a couple of weeks or so before it is intended to commence breeding. The birds may take soft food in only small amounts at this time, but even so it is important in bringing them into breeding condition and for the development of eggs or sperm.

It is pointless to attempt to breed from birds which are not in full breeding condition. This state can be recognized in males because they become particularly active and spend a great deal of time singing. Females in breeding condition are equally active. If they are separated from the males, but are still in earshot of them, they will call repeatedly to them. Unless colony breeding is contemplated, birds are paired in separate cages. It is dangerous to generalize about the breeding requirements of such a diverse group of birds as the parrot finches, some of which have not yet been bred in captivity. Nevertheless, successes so far suggest that they have many breeding requirements in common. For example, those species which are bred regularly will accept either the standard half-fronted finch nesting boxes, approximately 15 × 15 × 15 cm (6 × 6 × 6 in), or the rectangular boxes with a 4cm (1½ in) bobhole, of the kind supplied to breeding budgerigars.

Coarse dried grass, with some soft grass and perhaps feathers for those species which line their nests, and coconut fibre are normally provided as nesting materials. In most parrot finches, the male carries materials to the nest and the female spends her time inside the nest, weaving the materials into the desired shape. Clutch size varies from species to species, but incubation lasts for about 13-14 days in all of them. Once the young have hatched, soft food and/or other protein-rich foods are supplied regularly, preferably twice a day. The second feed should be given in the evening so that the crops of the young birds are filled before nightfall.

When eggs or young are expected, nest-box inspection is largely a matter of judgement, depending on the temperament of the birds. It is probably better to err on the side of caution, especially in the early stages of nest-building or egg-laying. Regular examination of young does, however, enable the early diagnosis of disease or other problems, and gives the opportunity to remove the corpses of any young which have died, before they become a health hazard to the whole brood. Healthy nestlings are plump and have a characteristically shiny skin. A full crop is an obvious sign that they are being fed by their parents. Young which are being neglected can be transferred to Bengalese Finch foster parents (if they are available; see below) or given supplementary hand-feeding. The technique for doing this is described in Evans & Fidler (1986).

It is important to examine the condition of the nest and the droppings in it, as well as the nestlings. The droppings of healthy nestlings are greyish with black centres. Those with the appearance of oatmeal indicate that the young are constipated, probably because they are being given dry seed by their parents. The remedy is to remove all dry seed and give the parents only soaked seed. Wet droppings which contaminate the young and the nest are a sure sign of diarrhoea. Antibiotics will usually cure this if they are added to the parents' drinking water. A 'universal antibiotic mix', which has proved successful in the past, consists of 13 parts of 5 per cent terramycin, one part of 70 per cent neomycin, and one part of multi-vitamin supplement. This is mixed at the rate of 0.4 gm in 120 ml of drinking water.

Fledging and Weaning

Young birds are sometimes lost at the time of fledging because one or two nestlings leave the nest prematurely. The parents may then feed only the new fledglings, ignoring the rest of the brood, or feed only those remaining in the nest. Within the controlled environment of the birdroom, the policy of one out all out can be adopted, once it has been ascertained that the early fledglings will not remain in the nest even if they are replaced in it. Those remaining in the nest when their broodmates have fledged should be removed from it and placed on the floor of the cage. The perches should be lowered to within about 7 cm (2¾ in) of the floor so that the parents must perch close to their young. They are then more likely to react to their begging calls.

Young parrot finches become independent of their parents about 35 days after hatching. Soon after this they should be taken away from them and transferred to a large stock/flight cage. Seed and water should be placed in containers on the floor of the cage, in addition to the usual hoppers, until it is certain that the young birds are familiar with the drinking and feeding places. Millet sprays, germinating seed and soft food (or live food) should also be provided. Bathing water is not advisable at first, because young birds may become chilled after bathing, or may occasionally drown, even in shallow water.

Juveniles moult gradually into adult plumage over a period of months (the time depends on the species). This is a difficult time for the young birds since the growth of feathers places a heavy drain on their protein reserves. Soft food should therefore be provided daily, at the rate of about half a teaspoon per bird, together with vitamin and mineral supplements, until the moult is complete.

Bengalese Finches as Foster Parents

Many finch breeders use Bengalese Finches as foster parents to rear parrot finches. The parrot-finch eggs are placed under Bengalese Finches which incubate them and subsequently carry out full parental duties (the techniques are described in full in Evans & Fidler, 1986). There are two particular advantages of foster-rearing. Firstly, good strains of Bengalese Finches are exceptionally reliable parents, so that they improve the chances of rearing young. Secondly, since parrot finches which are deprived of one clutch of eggs will usually lay another within a couple of weeks, the process greatly increases the number of offspring which can be reared from one pair of birds in a single season. As Evans & Fidler (1986) have stressed, however, there are also dangers in employing this breeding technique. There is widespread concern that it may lead to the production of generations of birds which are of inferior quality to their parents, and to stock which is incapable of rearing its own young. Imprinting is another widely discussed concern but, at least in the case of estrildid finches, it does not seem to affect breeding performance. Foster-reared Gouldian Finches, for example, are as capable of breeding successfully as those reared by natural parents. Whatever the pros and cons, however, there can be little doubt that, in the long term, the use of Bengalese Finches in this way is undesirable. Aviculturists must surely aim to establish strains of birds which are capable of rearing their own young.

6

Bamboo Parrot Finch,
Erythrura hyperythra

The Bamboo Parrot Finch has possibly the most charming personality of all the parrot finches. It is quiet and tame, except while breeding when it becomes reclusive. It was first described by Reichenbach in 1862, from a museum specimen which had supposedly been collected in New Guinea. This is outside the range which it is now known to occupy, so presumably the specimen had been wrongly labelled. Subsequently, a second specimen was described in 1883 by Vorderman. This time the location had been more accurately recorded: it had been collected in western Java. There are now eight recognized sub-species of the Bamboo Parrot Finch, occurring in a wide geographic range.

The description of the sub-species *E. hyperythra brunneiventris*, which is found in Mindanao and Luzon, is as follows: the upperparts are mossy green which contrasts with the warm buff colour of the breast, face and throat. The front of the forehead is black and the rest of the forehead and front of the crown are turquoise blue. The bill is black. Sexing can seem an impossible task at first, but with practice becomes relatively simple. The female has a thin black line on the lower forehead, rather than the dark, almost navy blue, of the male's 'pince-nez'. Furthermore, the blue of the male's forehead extends back behind the eyes, while that of the female finishes before it reaches eye level. Juveniles lack blue on the head, have pale body plumage and yellow bills.

Fig. 4 *Bamboo Parrot Finch. The Greentail is similar in appearance.
The size of this bird's feet indicate that it is a juvenile.*

The seven remaining sub-species differ from *E. hyperythra brunneiventris* in the following ways:

E. hyperythra borneensis, which inhabits Borneo, is more yellowish-green, and the buff-coloured areas, except those of the breast, are generally paler. The blue of the forehead extends further back, well beyond the level of the eyes.

E.h. microrhyncha, which comes from Celebes, has less blue on the head, and that which occurs has a greenish tinge.

E.h. malayana, is from Peninsula Malaysia. It is more yellowish-green above and the buff-coloured areas have a yellowish tinge.

E.h. intermedia comes from Lombok. It has duller blue on the forehead and yellowish-green wing coverts.

E.h. hyperythra is from western Java. It has an intensely coloured golden-buff rump.

E.h. obscura, from Flores and Sumbawa, has duller blue on the forehead and a yellowish-green body colour.

E.h. ernstmayri, from south Celebes, has less extensive blue on the forehead and yellowish-green body colour.

The Bamboo Parrot Finch is usually seen in forest clearings and on the edges of forests, especially where bamboo is abundant. It often occurs at relatively high altitudes, between 1,000 and 3,000 m (3,280-9,840 ft), but on some islands it occurs as low as 300 m (980 ft) above sea level. As we have already seen in Chapter 2, its precise range depends on the presence or absence of species with which it is in competition. It is a specialist feeder on bamboo seeds, but may also take insects from time to time.

Van Balen (1987) describes its breeding habits from observations at two nests at a site in western Java. One was situated close to the top of a tree, 4 m (13 ft) high, near the forest edge. The outer part of the nest consisted of fine twigs and roots, and the inner part of fine fibres and grass leaves. The other nest was about 12 m (39 ft) above the ground in a tree 25 m (82 ft) high, which was almost branchless and without leaves. The entrance was hidden in a clump of ferns, orchids and mosses. One member of the pair which constructed this nest, probably the male, carried nesting materials to it. The other bird, presumably the female, remained inside the nest, arranging the materials. Although Van Balen visited this nest regularly, and the birds were often seen near it, he was not certain that their attempt to breed was successful.

Avicultural Notes

Several aviculturists have been successful in breeding the Bamboo Parrot Finch, but it is still not fully established. One problem seems to be in finding a suitable substitute diet for its natural one (see below).

The species was exhibited in Berlin Zoo in 1930, but it did not become well known in aviculture until much later. Dr Heinrich Bregulla brought back some wild-caught individuals of the sub-species *E. hyperythra brunneiventris* in 1965, and these were kept by two experts: Dr Romauld Burkhard and Dr Vincenz Ziswiler.

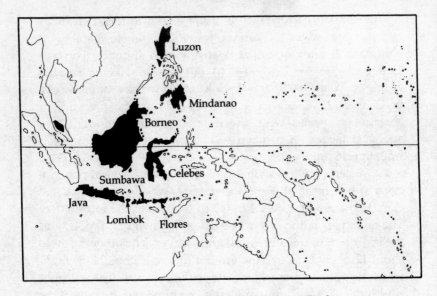

Fig. 5 Distribution of the Bamboo Parrot Finch.

The birds survived on a diet of Italian millet, but failed to breed. Nests were built and eggs laid, but the breeding cycle never progressed further than this.

Imports of the sub-species *E. hyperythra microrhyncha* followed in 1981, and once again Dr Burkhard kept some of them in captivity. He found that they would take a varied diet of seeds, as well as animal food in the form of flour moth larvae, maggots and hard-boiled eggs. He succeeded in breeding them in a well-planted aviary, measuring 3 × 5 m (10 × 16 ft), containing fir trees, Scots pine and beech trees. Two pairs of Bamboo Parrot Finches shared this accommodation with Chestnut-breasted Mannikins, Waxbills and Gouldian Finches. One pair of parrot finches started to breed in a half-open nest box. They laid five eggs, two of which hatched, but the young did not survive to the fledging stage. The second pair built their nest, which measured 16 × 12 cm (6¼ × 4¾ in) on the outside with an entrance hole 2 cm (¾ in) in diameter, in a bush. Three young birds fledged from it.

One of the authors (MEF) was the first person to breed this species in the United Kingdom. Cage breeding was employed initially, and the first fledgling left the nest in February 1982. That year, two birds were reared from three clutches. In the 1983 season, Burkhard's successful technique of colony breeding in planted aviaries was tried, but this was a total failure; no young at all were reared. An attempt to breed these parrot finches in communal indoor aviaries was equally unsuccessful. Four pairs were then separated from each other and housed in cages measuring 75 × 20 × 80 cm (30 × 8 × 31 in). One of these pairs, however, shared its cage with some Black-capped Zosterops. Fruit was provided for the latter birds and, within a week, the parrot finches were avidly sharing this food with them. Two weeks later courtship and nest-building activity was observed, followed by egg-laying. The eggs were transferred to Bengalese Finch foster parents, which successfully reared the young which hatched from them.

The remaining pairs were reluctant to take fruit when this was first offered to them, but were eventually persuaded to take it when it was liquidized and mixed with soft food. Breeding successes followed soon afterwards. The provision of plenty of perches, some of them natural twiggy ones, also appears to be an important requirement for breeding. Males which are ready to breed 'drive' females from perch to perch, and this process may be necessary to bring their mates into breeding condition. The male carries a piece of nesting material while he drives his mate and she evidently indicates her acceptance by taking it from him. Frenzied nest-building starts almost immediately afterwards.

Paul and Lucy Horner (1989) not only bred this species in Wales but, like Dr Burkhard, bred them successfully in an outdoor, planted aviary. They made detailed observations of the behaviour and habits of their stock, which had access to a flight measuring approximately 6 × 1.5 m (19½ × 5 ft). The inhabitants of this aviary spent a great deal of time foraging on the ground, often in groups, scratching at the soil. They perched acrobatically, sometimes hanging vertically by one leg from perches and feeding while doing so. They were most active in the evenings and avoided strong light or even hazy sun, possibly as a result of adaptations to low light intensities in their natural, upland habitats. Bathing was a popular activity, occurring four or five times per day in water provided for them; rain-bathing also occurred during showers of rain, even on cold, windy days.

The Horners found that pair bonds were tight in Bamboo Parrot Finches (unlike most parrot finches) and individuals were normally only prepared to remate after the death of the original partner. Nests were constructed with leaves, grasses, plant shoots and roots, and strands of shredded bamboo leaves. They were defended actively until eggs were laid, when pairs became far more tolerant of other birds in the vicinity. The usual clutch size was between three and five eggs. Incubation duties were shared during the day, but females always incubated at night. Some females stopped incubating when their young were seven or eight days old (others continued for longer than this) and during cold spells of weather; this resulted in the death of nestlings. Fledging occurred between 24 and 28 days, but pairs often constructed a second nest at a new site, and laid eggs in it, before this happened. In such cases, the female left further parental duties for the first brood entirely to the male. She concentrated her attention on the new clutch of eggs.

One problem with parrot finches is that birds which are not in breeding condition go into a perpetual pin feather moult, and difficulty often arises in getting males and females out of this (i.e. into breeding condition) at the same time. A good technique is to keep separate groups of males and females (say four to six birds in each group) and then introduce male-female pairs as and when birds stop moulting. Bamboo Parrot Finches are secretive when nesting and should be given a cage in a quiet corner of the birdroom A sheet of paper forming a curtain over the area of the cage in which the nest box is positioned gives extra seclusion.

7

Pin-tailed Parrot Finch, *Erythrura prasina*

Fig. 6 Pin-tailed Parrot Finch.

Although the Pin-tailed Parrot Finch was the first member of the group to be described (Sparrman, 1788), surprisingly little is known about either its habits in the wild or its requirements in aviculture. This is in spite of its abundance in some parts of its natural range and its importation in large numbers for the cage bird market. It has a wide geographic range, occurring as two recognized sub-species: *E. prasina prasina*, which inhabits Java, Sumatra, Malaysia, Thailand, western Laos, Vietnam and

Cambodia, and *E. prasina coelica*, which is restricted to Borneo.

The Pin-tailed Parrot Finch is one of the most beautiful members of the genus. *E. prasina prasina* has a dull cobalt-blue face mask, dark green upperparts, a scarlet rump and upper tail coverts, and buff underparts with a large red patch on the lower breast and belly. The female is generally less brightly coloured, lacks the blue face mask and has a shorter tail than the male. Juveniles are similar to females, but greyer and generally duller. There is a naturally occurring mutant, which seems to occur in about 8-10 per cent of imported birds, and in which the areas of red coloration are replaced by yellow. Some writers have suggested that it is much more common in females than in males. *E. prasina coelica* is more brightly coloured than *E. prasina prasina* and the blue of the male's face mask extends over the upper breast. Female *E. prasina coelica* have blue on the throat and breast.

This species occurs along forest edges and in bamboo thickets, and these are presumably its original habitats. Grass seeds are evidently the major component of the diet in birds living here, although they will sometimes feed on the seed heads of bamboos. They also exploit rice plantations and have become pests in some parts of their range, feeding exclusively on rice. In Borneo, Pin-tailed Parrot Finches can reach plague proportions, and the farming calendar is organized so that the rice crop is ripe, and can be harvested, before the birds, which are evidently migratory, arrive to devour it.

Nests are constructed in thickets or in tree trunks which are overgrown with lianas. The nest can be situated from about 1 to 70 m (230 ft) above the ground. It is spherical in shape and made from plant fibres. There is a side entrance. The clutch size is usually between four and six eggs.

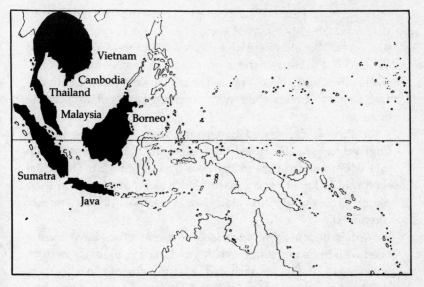

Fig. 7 Distribution of the Pin-tailed Parrot Finch.

Avicultural Notes

Pin-tailed Parrot Finches are excellent aviary subjects. They are swift and acrobatic in flight and appear more confident in aviaries than in cages. Rice is often a staple part of their diet in captivity. Traders frequently supply it as the major food for shipments of birds and most successful breeders have included it as a dietary supplement. Pin-tailed Parrot Finches have proved a difficult species to breed in the past, however, and it is only in recent years that regular successes are being reported.

Restall (1983) kept these birds successfully without breeding them. He supplied his stock with soaked and dry rice, clipped oats, canary seed and hemp. Various millets were ignored. His parrot finches were equally fussy about fruit: sliced orange was taken but apple, banana and pear were not. Mealworms and maggots were provided but not taken.

There had, however, been earlier breeding successes in

63

Europe. Herr Horst Wagner bred the species in Germany in 1913, and roughly 50 years later, Herr F. Karl reported further successes. The latter kept his birds at a minimum temperature of 25° C (77° F). He fed them on canary seeds, dehusked oats, white millet and millet spray, all of which were offered both dry and soaked. Green food was provided, as well as seeding grasses.

Mr P.A.M. Fry reared two young from a breeding pair in England in 1984. He noted the typical change to a protein-rich diet when young were in the nest (see Chapter 3). The usual seed mix of millets and canary seed was ignored and, in their place, groats and soft food (with additions) were readily consumed.

Further encouraging successes in recent years have mostly been with birds in planted aviaries and in large flight cages. Rice (dry and soaked) are included as supplements in the diets provided by most successful breeders, as are ample supplies of green food (especially chickweed). Some breeders find that, contrary to the experiences of earlier aviculturists, live food is taken when young are in the nest. It is probably not essential, however, since at least some of them have been successful when only soft food has been provided. However, a general consensus is forming among aviculturists that sprouted seed of one sort or another is important. Blue-faced Parrot Finches have sometimes been used to foster-rear Pin-tailed Parrot Finches.

This species suffers from the same problem as the Bamboo Parrot Finch in coming into a pin moult as it goes out of breeding condition. The technique of keeping separate groups of males and females and then pairing birds when they are ready to breed, which was recommended for the Bamboo Parrot Finch, is therefore also suitable for the Pin-tailed Parrot Finch. Secluded nest sites are preferred. Dried grass and sizal, coconut fibres and moss may be utilized as nesting materials. The clutch size varies between two and five; incubation lasts for 12-14 days; young fledge about 21 days after hatching. The young reach sexual maturity at the age of about six or seven months.

Pin-tailed Parrot Finch.

Bamboo Parrot Finch. The conspicuous pin feathers show that the bird is in the process of moulting.

A pair of Blue-faced Parrot Finches.

Hand feeding a nestling Blue-faced Parrot Finch.

Lutino Blue-faced Parrot Finch.

Manila Parrot Finches.

Red-headed Parrot Finch.

Male and female sea-green mutation of the Red-headed Parrot Finch.

Pied mutation of Red-headed Parrot Finch.

Peale's Parrot Finch.

Katanglad Parrot Finch.

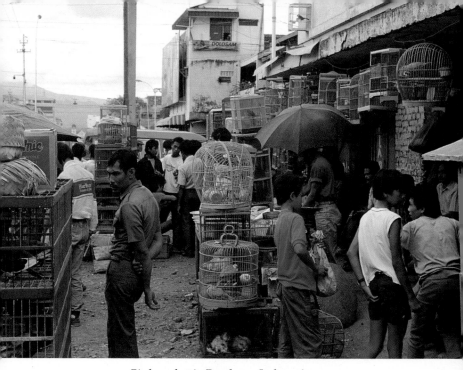

Bird market in Bandung, Indonesia.

Over-crowded cages in the bird market in Jakarta, Indonesia.

Tropical rain forest in western Java. Tragically, only tiny areas of rain forest now remain on Java.

8

Manila Parrot Finch,
Erythrura viridifacies

Fig. 8 Manila Parrot Finch.

Although the Manila Parrot Finch was not described until 1937, it was known before this time. Hachisuka and Delacour (1937) describe how Mr E. H. Taylor, a resident of the town of Los Banos near Manila, found the corpses of ten small birds which had flown suicidally into the wire netting surrounding his tennis court in June 1926. They were almost certainly Manila Parrot Finches, as were large numbers of parrot finches which

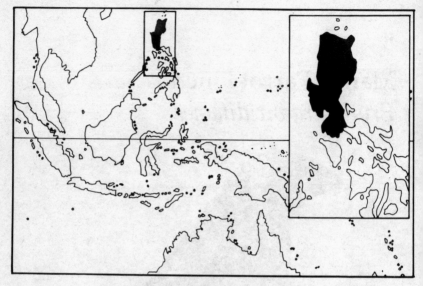

Fig. 9 Distribution of the Manila Parrot Finch. The inset shows an enlargement of Luzon in the Philippines.

were offered for sale in the Manila Bird Market 15 years later. Several hundred of these birds, still unidentified, were exported from Manila to San Francisco in 1936.

The Manila Parrot Finch is the only parrot finch which has an entirely green head. The general body colour is grass-green, darker on the upperside. The median tail coverts are an intense red. The male has a greyish breast, buff and green belly and buff abdomen. Juveniles have light buff undersides. Males have noticeably longer tails than females, and are slightly brighter and lighter in coloration.

This species is seen infrequently in the wild and therefore little is known about its habits. It is restricted to Luzon in the Philippines, where it occurs in savanna, along the edges of forests and among bamboo stands. Grass, *Casuarina* and possibly bamboo seeds are included in the diet. Large flocks sometimes occur where grasses and bamboos are seeding.

Avicultural Notes

Importation of birds has occurred from time to time, but with no success in establishing them in captivity. About 200 pairs were imported into Europe in 1966. Dr R. Burkhard kept some of them and found they would take a variety of seeds but that mealworms and soft food were ignored. Mineral and vitamin supplements were added to the drinking water, but he did not succeed in breeding them.

An import of birds into England in 1980 probably suffered a similar fate. Mr I. Morley (1984) obtained eight of them but, despite his successes with other parrot finches, he was unable to breed from them. One pair showed courtship behaviour and the start of nest-building, but got no further in the breeding cycle. Mr Morley complained of general inactivity in his birds and excessive growth of claws, which required regular clipping.

Our own experiences with this species are similar to those described above, except that we found that the birds would take soft food. A globular nest of grasses and coconut fibre was constructed in a half-front nest box, but no eggs were laid.

9

Tri-coloured Parrot Finch,
Erythrura tricolor

Fig. 10 Tri-coloured Parrot Finch.

Little is known about this species, which comes from Timor and nearby islands in Indonesia. The head and breast of the male are deep cobalt-blue, while the fringes of the sides of the head, belly and flanks, are a lighter shade of blue. The beak and wings are moss-green. Upper tail coverts are bright red. The head and breast of the female are turquoise and faded green in colour, with a grey area in the middle of the breast and belly. Upper tail coverts are red-orange. The upper side of juveniles is dark green.

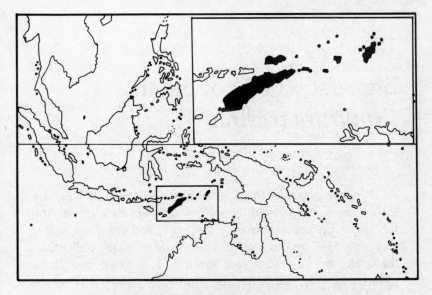

*Fig. 11 Distribution of the Tri-coloured Parrot Finch. The inset shows
an enlargement of Timor in Indonesia and nearby islands.*

These birds search for food in trees and usually nest in the
tops of coconut palms.

The species is unknown to aviculture.

10

Blue-faced Parrot Finch,
Erythrura trichroa

As its name suggests, this species has a conspicuous blue face mask. The upperparts of the male's body are dark green. The throat and underparts are a lighter green, and the rump, upper and central tail coverts are red. The female is usually duller than the male and the blue face mask is less extensive. These differences can, however, be unreliable, especially when comparisons are made between different sub-species (see below). Juveniles have little or no blue on the head and have yellow bills (rather than the black ones of adults).

The Blue-faced Parrot Finch occupies a wide geographic range, extending, from north to south, from the Caroline Islands to the north-east tip of Australia and, from west to east, from Celebes to Vanuatu (formerly New Hebrides). There are a number of isolated populations and Ziswiler et al. (1972) recognized ten sub-species. They differ from one another in the details of their coloration and, in at least some cases, body measurements. The habits of only two sub-species are well-known. These are *E. trichroa sigillifera*, which comes from north-east Australia and New Guinea, and *E. trichroa cyanofrons*, which inhabits Vanuatu and nearby islands. Differences between them are considerable. *E. trichroa cyanofrons* has become highly successful in habitats which have been modified by people, and occurs in areas such as the edges of roads, garden plantations and paddocks, as well as forest clearings, but *E. trichroa sigillifera* is confined mainly to remaining patches of rain forest in north-east Australia (Marshall, 1948) and to secondary

Fig. 12 *Blue-faced Parrot Finch.*

bushland, forest clearings and the edges of forests in New Guinea (Mayr, 1931). *E. trichroa cyanofrons* feeds primarily on grass seeds, with some herbaceous seeds in its diet, while *E. trichroa sigillifera* is believed to feed mainly on grass and ripe bamboo seeds.

Table 5 Differences in the coloration of some parts of the body of the sub-species of the Blue-faced Parrot Finch. (Data from Ziswiler et al., 1972)

Sub-species	Distribution	Head	Upperparts	Underparts	Upper tail coverts
E. t. cyanofrons	Vanuatu	deep cobalt	gold shimmer near head	grass-green	dark red
E. t. sanfordi	Celebes	violet blue	gold shimmer near head	yellow-green	red-orange
E. t. modesta	N. Moluccas	deep cobalt	shimmer on back	grass-green	dark red

Parrot Finches

Sub-species	Distribution	Head	Upper parts	Under parts	Upper tail coverts
E. t. pinaiae	S. Moluccas	deep cobalt	bluish-green	lighter bluish-green	yellow-orange
E. t. sigillifera	New Guinea N.E. Australia	deep cobalt	minimal gold shimmer	bluish-green	dark red
E. t. eichhorni	Bismarck Archipelago	cobalt	minimal gold shimmer	grass-green	red-orange
E. t. pelewensis	Palau Islands	deep cobalt	gold shimmer on nape	blue shimmer	bright red
E. t. trichroa	E. Caroline Islands	lighter blue	intense gold shimmer on nape	grass-green	dark red
E. t. woodfordi	Solomon Islands	cobalt	no gold shimmer	ligher bluish-green	yellow-orange
E. t. clara	Central Caroline Islands	deep cobalt	gold shimmer on nape	yellow-green	red-orange

Table 6 Differences in body measurements in three sub-species of the Blue-faced Parrot Finch. Weights are in grams; lengths in millimetres (Data from Ziswiler et al., 1972)

Sub-species	Weight	Head-trunk	Tail	Wing	Bill Length	Height
E. t. cyanofrons	8.5-9.5	78-81	42-48	54-58	9	7
E. t. pinaiae	18	78	33	60-65	11	8
E. t. sigillifera	12-18.5	88-91	46-51	57-60	12	9

E. trichroa cyanofrons breeds mostly from October to February. It nests in holes in coralline rock, especially in places where the rock is covered with plant growth. It also nests in exposed roots of Banyan fig trees and in dense foliage. The nest chamber is large, measuring approximately 10 × 8 × 8 cm (4 × 3 × 3 in),

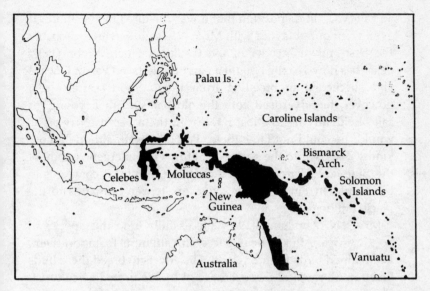

Fig. 13 Distribution of the Blue-faced Parrot Finch.

with an entrance tunnel 3.5 cm (1⅓ in) long. Fine leaves and stems are used as nesting materials, but there is no nest lining. Marshall (1948) describes a single nest of *E. trichroa sigillifera* in the top of a tree 7 m (23 ft) high. The breeding chamber had a diameter of 7.5 cm (3 in); it was lined with grass. Mosses and fungus threads were used as the main nesting materials.

Nests of *E. trichroa cyanofrons* usually contain three, some-times four, young birds (Ziswiler et al. 1972). There were three eggs in the nest of *E. trichroa sigillifera* described by Marshall (1948), but this may not have been a full clutch.

Avicultural Notes

The Blue-faced Parrot Finch is now one of the easiest members of the parrot finch group to breed and maintain in captivity. This has not always been the case. It was once regarded as so wild and nervous in disposition that it was unsuited to aviculture. It even went out of favour with Mr P.W. Teague, who is probably the best-known breeder of the Gouldian Finch. Webb (1932) describes how Teague bought a pair of Blue-faced Parrot Finches and succeeded in breeding from them. Shortly afterwards, however, he advertised both the old pair and their young for sale. Evidently he had lost interest in them because, try as he would, he could not tame them. Webb himself, although more kindly disposed to the species, confirms the energetic nature of the Blue-faced Parrot Finch. According to him, it compares to the Gouldian Finch as the active fox terrier compares to the placid bulldog.

Mr C. N. Abrahams (1939) successfully bred this species in South Africa. After some unsuccessful attempts to import them, he obtained birds from England. His efforts to breed these birds illustrate the typical perseverance of the dedicated aviculturist. The first pair was released into an aviary containing Gouldian Finches, Hooded Siskins and Bicheno Finches. Unfortunately, their attempt to breed resulted in disaster. A pair of Gouldian Finches took over the Parrot Finch nest, causing the death of two well-developed youngsters. The following season, a second pair of Blue-faced Parrot Finches was released into an aviary, this time a well-planted one which they had to themselves. The first sign of breeding success was when the male bird started to gorge himself heavily on termites. This bird became so tame at this time (unlike Teague's birds) that he would fly down and perch on the pot which contained the termites while it was being placed in the aviary. The begging calls of young birds were heard soon afterwards. Gradually these became louder until four healthy young fledged. The pair re-nested and that season raised a total of 14 young, 12 of which survived to maturity. The following year, the same pair reared another 14 young. This time all of them reached maturity.

Nowadays, the Blue-faced Parrot Finch is well established as a good aviary and cage bird. Many young are foster-reared by Bengalese Finch parents, but these parrot finches are such excellent parents themselves that they have even been used as foster parents for more difficult parrot finches (see Chapter 7).

The species will thrive on a standard foreign finch mix of millets and canary seed during the non-breeding season. A suitable soft food (or live food) should, however, be provided while birds are breeding and when they are in the process of moulting. Birds between the ages of nine months and two years often provide the best breeding results. Box-type cages, measuring 50 × 50 × 50 cm (20 × 20 × 20 in), are suitable breeding cages, and while a variety of nest boxes may be used, the half-open front style is most readily accepted. Long pieces of dried grass are suitable materials for nest construction, with soft grass or coconut fibres for nest lining. The usual clutch is five, varying from three to seven eggs. Hatching occurs after 13 or 14 days of incubation, and young fledge 20-21 days later. Many successful breeders provide soft food for the first nine days after young hatch and then supplement this with the provision of soaked (germinating) seed from days 9 to 35. Young are then weaned from their parents. They moult into adult plumage in three to five months.

Abrahams (1939) discovered that nests were perfectly clean after young had fledged from them. He did not make direct observations of nest hygiene, but Ziswiler et al. (1972) describe how young (of this and other parrot finches) thrust their hindquarters out of the nest chamber while defecating and, in this way, prevent it from becoming contaminated. It has also been reported that parents remove droppings from nests.

A lutino mutation appeared in France in 1982, and has been quickly established in the rest of Europe. It is sex-linked.

11

Papuan Parrot Finch, *Erythrura papuana*

Fig. 14 Papuan Parrot Finch.

The rare Papuan Parrot Finch resembles the Blue-faced Parrot Finch, especially the sub-species *E. trichroa sigillifera*. The blue face mask of the male, however, extends further beyond the eyes than that of the latter species, and the upper part of the throat is also blue. The Papuan Parrot Finch is also a larger and heavier bird than *E. trichroa sigillifera*, with longer wings and a stouter bill (Table 6). The female Papuan Parrot Finch has a less

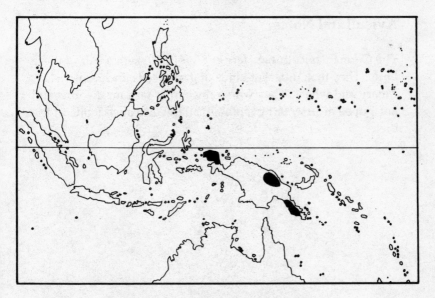

Fig. 15 Distribution of the Papuan Parrot Finch.

extensive face mask than the male, and is generally paler in coloration.

This species is restricted to New Guinea. It is a mountain bird, occurring mainly in the forest and in secondary growth along the edges of forests. Its range coincides with that of the Blue-faced Parrot Finch (*E. trichroa sigillifera*) but the two species are separated by living at different altitudes. The Papuan Parrot Finch lives at altitudes between 1,000 and 2,000 m (3,280-6,560 ft), while the Blue-faced Parrot Finch occurs above this. Diamond (1972) suggests that New Guinea was invaded first by the Papuan Parrot Finch, but that it is in the process of being gradually replaced by the more recently arrived Blue-faced Parrot Finch. It survives at only a few localities.

Feeding and breeding habits are virtually unknown. Ziswiler et al. (1972) believe, on the basis of the results of food-selection experiments with captured birds, that it is probably a fig-seed eater.

Avicultural Notes

The German aviculturist Herr R. Neff (1970) kept a pair of these birds. They took different kinds of grass seeds, including millet, canary and wheat. They were reluctant to take mealworms and ant pupae at first, but eventually adapted to such foods in the diet.

12
Katanglad Parrot Finch,
Erythrura coloria

Fig. 16 Katanglad Parrot Finch.

The Katanglad Parrot Finch was not discovered until 1960 and was not described until the following year, by Rabor and Ripley. It remained undiscovered for so long because it is restricted to the remote slopes of Mount Katanglad, which stands in the central part of the Philippine island of Mindanao.

The male is similar in appearance to the Blue-faced Parrot Finch, except for an orange/red collar on each side of the head and neck. The face mask is cobalt-blue, the body coloration is dark green and the lower rump and upper tail coverts are red. Young females were slightly paler in coloration than males and the red neck collars are smaller. Females tend to darken in general coloration as they age, so that older ones are less easy to distinguish from males. Body measurements are similar between

the sexes so they, too, are an unreliable guide for sexing birds.
Juveniles lack the red neck collar of adults, and are dull moss-
green in colour. Their bills are yellow, not black like those of
adults.

Katanglad Parrot Finches occur on mountain slopes up to
1,600 m (5,250 ft) above sea level in their natural habitat. They
are seen at the forest edge or in clearings where there are grasses
or herbaceous plants. Birds forage on the ground or by hanging
from plant stems close to the ground. They feed mostly on the
seeds of grasses and bamboos, as well as insects. Individuals
spend most daylight hours in open valleys, but congregate in
flocks in the evenings before entering forested areas, where
presumably they roost.

Table 7 A comparison of various body measurements of male and
female Katanglad Parrot Finches. Lengths are expressed in millimetres
and weights in grams. (Data from Ziswiler et al., 1972)

Measurement	*Males*	*Females*
Number measured	14	8
Head-trunk	74.1	76.6
Tail	37.0	34.4
Wing	56.4	56.2
Bill length	11.5	11.5
height	8.6	8.5
Weight	10.1	10.8

Avicultural Notes

Katanglad Parrot Finches have charming personalities and seem
to be naturally tamer and more confiding than any of the other
parrot finches. They are less active than most of their relatives
and spend a far greater proportion of their time on the ground.
They adapt readily to either aviary or cage conditions. Care
should be taken when furnishing quarters for them, as they

have unusually long legs, which are easily damaged. They should not, for example, be caged with over-robust birds when being transported, and trouble should be taken to ensure that there is no loose wire or other obstruction in their travelling boxes or cages, on which legs could become caught.

Dr R. Burkhard of Zurich received a shipment of about 60 birds from Dr Heinrich Bregulla in 1964. He managed to keep 14 pairs and bred successfully from them. He fed his birds mostly on canary seed, spray millet, mealworms and ant pupae. Pairs which were breeding young took sprouted canary seed, seeding grasses, soft food and ant pupae. Burkhard's birds used coconut fibres and grass stems to construct nests and built them in half-open nest boxes. The nests were unlined. The usual clutch size was only two or three eggs. Incubation lasted for 12-13 days and young fledged about 21 days later, becoming independent two weeks afterwards. Birds matured rapidly, coming into breeding condition at the age of only about five months.

Burkhard passed on birds to other breeders, but early breeding successes were short-lived. Stocks dwindled and by 1980 only a few isolated birds remained. Most of these were of poor quality and, foolishly, some breeders hybridized their stock with the Blue-faced Parrot Finch. Fortunately, Dr Bregulla was able to visit Mount Katanglad again in 1983 and he then imported fresh stock into Europe. Even now, however, the species is still not fully established in captivity and is well deserving of special attention.

Our own experiences suggest that this species tends to become obese under caged conditions, especially if it is fed on excesses of seeds such as hemp, rape or niger. It is probably wise, therefore, to restrict them to a mix of canary seed and the usual millets. Soft food is evidently less fattening to these birds, and can therefore be provided as required. Green food is an important part of the diet and appears to enhance breeding performance.

Katanglad Parrot Finches do, nevertheless, make good

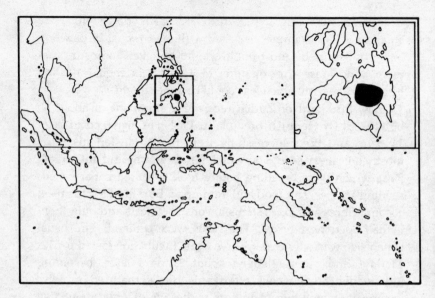

Fig. 17 Distribution of the Katanglad Parrot Finch. The inset shows an enlargement of Mindanao in the Philippines and nearby islands.

parents and will rear young successfully without recourse to the use of Bengalese Finches as foster parents. Colony breeding has proved successful. Under these conditions, pairs will nest readily in tubular baskets made with sheep wire netting: mesh of about 10 × 15 cm (4 × 6 in) measuring 1 m (tall) × 50 cm (diameter) (39 × 20 in). The baskets are stuffed with hawthorn branches and dried grass, and hung vertically in flights. Fist-sized holes are 'punched' into the nesting materials in order to encourage the birds to nest. Pairs may nest extremely close together, perhaps no more than 10-20 cm (4-8 in) apart, in such baskets, with little or no aggression between them.

It is important to introduce 'new blood' into colonies, however, because this species appears to succumb to problems connected with in-breeding (e.g. low fertility) over a few generations.

13

Red-headed Parrot Finch, *Erythrura psittacea*

Goodwin (1983) believes that the Red-headed Parrot Finch is the most beautiful member of the genus *Erythrura*. It has a striking colour scheme, is shapely and possesses an active personality. Webb (1932) would probably have shared this view. He described it as 'The most sprightly, vivacious little bundle of feathers that it is possible to imagine.'

The face, including the forehead, forecrown, throat and upper breast, is bright red, contrasting strongly with the bright green of the general body plumage. The rump, upper tail coverts and central tail feathers are also red. There are no consistent differences between the sexes, but aviculturists use the following guides (probably giving them about 90 per cent accuracy in sexing birds):

(i) The red coloration of the male covers a larger area than that of the female. The male's face mask, unlike that of the female, may extend beyond the line of the eyes in the head region and below the base of the wings in the breast region.

(ii) The lores of the male are blacker, wider and more distinctly defined than those of the female.

(iii) The fifth and sixth feathers of the tail are pointed in the male but rounded in the female.

(iv) Males in breeding condition spend a great deal of time singing.

The Red-headed Parrot Finch is restricted naturally to the island of New Caledonia. It has been reported on Vanuatu but

Fig. 18 Red-headed Parrot Finch.

probably exists there as a result of introductions by people. It has exploited habitats which have been modified by humans and, although it is seen close to forests, it is more common in plantations and gardens. Species which have been introduced into New Caledonia, such as the Red-eared Waxbill and the Chestnut-breasted Mannikin, have also adapted to cultivated parts of the island, and may compete with the Red-headed Parrot Finch for food and living space.

Red-headed Parrot Finches usually occur in pairs or in flocks of up to 20 birds. They forage from bush to bush, avoiding open spaces, and only occasionally alight on the ground to search for fallen seeds. They are skilful foragers, picking seeds and insects from flower heads while perched on narrow stems. They sometimes take grass seeds but probably only when herbaceous seeds are not available. Analyses of the crop contents of two

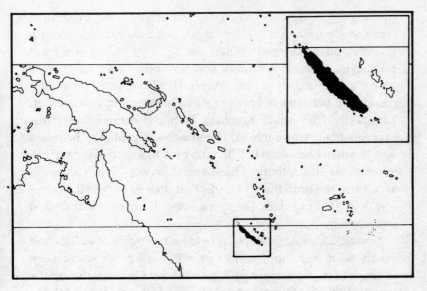

Fig. 19 Distribution of the Red-headed Parrot Finch. The inset shows an enlargement of New Caledonia and nearby islands.

adults and two nestlings by Ziswiler et al. (1972) revealed the following: 60 per cent herb seeds; 20 per cent grass seeds; 20 per cent spiders and insects, especially insect larvae.

There appear to be two breeding seasons: one in September and the other in March. Globular nests, consisting of leaves, stems and fibrous bark, are constructed in hollows such as those in coral rock, in the tangled roots of trees, in tussocks of grass and in old walls. Clutches of four to six eggs are incubated for 13 days before they hatch. Three or four nestlings survive in most nests and fledge after about 21 days.

Avicultural Notes

Red-headed Parrot Finches have been kept in captivity since the end of the last century, with varying degrees of success. Diet, however, seems to be the single most important factor in catering for their needs. Savage (1897), for instance, bred them successfully on a rich diet of canary and millet seeds, seeding grasses and chickweed. When young were in the nest, ant pupae, mealworms and milk sop (i.e. bread and milk) were given as additional items. Webb (1932) reported a similar correlation between richness of diet and breeding success and, admittedly with small numbers of birds, demonstrated this experimentally (see Table 8). The most successful of all breeders was Norman Nicholson (1950), who bred this species through 18 generations in captivity. Other breeders were less successful and it was not until the mid-1970s that, thanks to the efforts of a few dedicated breeders, the species was thoroughly established in aviculture.

Nowadays, most breeders provide a basic diet of millets and canary seed, but supplement this with herbaceous seeds, such as those of niger, hemp and maw. Soft food is given during the breeding season. Some, but not all, breeders include live food in the diet when young are being reared.

This species will nest at any time of year as long as birds are in breeding condition. They mature early and young adults may be ready to breed within six to eight weeks of moulting out of juvenile plumage. They are often highly fertile at this age. Pair compatibility is sometimes a problem if individuals are not allowed to select their own mates.

Clutch size varies between three and seven. Eggs are incubated for 13 or 14 days before hatching, and young fledge about 21 days later. They become independent when about 33-35 days old.

Red-headed Parrot Finches are good aviary subjects. They are hardy birds and, if provided with a heated shelter during winter months in temperate climates, can be left in an outdoor aviary all year round. They prefer to nest in deep cover in planted aviaries. Although they live peacefully with other species in mixed collections, they are unassertive and may, for example, suffer from more domineering species robbing their nests for nesting materials.

There are two established mutations of the Red-headed Parrot Finch. A pied form, in which patches of green coloration are replaced with yellow, was first recorded in Holland in the late 1970s and is now widely available. Subsequently, a sea-green mutation has been established. It has an orange head and the body colour is sea-green. Mogg (1988) describes two other mutations which have been less successful. A yellow-headed mutant was reported in Denmark in the 1940s but 'disappeared' after three or four years. An orange-headed variety, which occurred in New Zealand roughly ten years later, suffered a similar fate.

Table 8 The results of an experiment carried out by Mr P.B.Webb in 1932 on diet and breeding success in Red-headed Parrot Finches.

Pair	Food Supplied	Food Not Supplied	Results
1 Old pair which had reared 3 young in 1931	canary seed white millet Indian millet soaked seed	mealworms insectile mixture cod liver oil	One nest of 4 eggs; 2 hatched but young died
2 Female bred in 1931 by above pair; male imported	canary seed white millet Indian millet millet sprays insectile mixture when rearing young	mealworms cod liver oil	Four nests; average 2.8 eggs. No young reared to fledging
3 Female bred in 1931 by pair (1) above; male imported. Two unpaired males in same aviary	canary seed white millet Indian millet millet sprays insectile mixture mealworms cod liver oil soaked seed		Two nests, each with 4 eggs; 8 young fledged; 4 reared to independence

14

Royal Parrot Finch,
Erythrura cyaneovirens

Claims that the Red-headed Parrot Finch is the most beautiful member of the genus (see Chapter 13) do not go unchallenged. Walter Goodfellow (1934) extolled the beauty of the Royal Parrot Finch when he wrote,

> When in full plumage I think that there is no doubt that it is the most beautiful finch known. Gouldians look pale and washed out in comparison with the striking contrast of the scarlet, blue and green of the regias.

Goodfellow was writing about individuals of the sub-species of the Royal Parrot Finch *(E. cyaneovirens regia)* which come from Vanuatu. The head of the male has blackish lores but is otherwise deep scarlet red. The rump and upper tail coverts are also red. The throat is mauve/blue and the neck, upper mantle and breast are bright blue. The back, wings, belly and flanks are green. The female is similar to the male but the blue on the neck and breast may be less bright. The heads of juveniles are cobalt or greyish-blue rather than red and the general body plumage is dark green. Juveniles have yellow bills, whereas adults have black bills.

There are four other sub-species, two from Vanuatu and two from islands of Western Samoa, more than 1,600 km (1,000 miles) away.

Fig. 20 Royal Parrot Finch.

E. cyaneovirens serena

This sub-species differs from *E.c. regia* in that the upperparts are predominantly green; the area of blue is restricted to a narrow band round the neck. It once inhabited Aneiteum Island but the rain forest there has been cleared and, despite extensive searches, it has not been recorded for many years. It is probably extinct.

E. cyaneovirens efatensis

This sub-species is similar to *E. c. serena*, but the red areas of plumage are relatively dark. Du Pont (1972) questioned the validity of separating *E. c. efatensis* from *E. c. serena* as a sub-species on the basis of colour differences. Colour is variable and therefore an unreliable character on which to base comparisons, especially of Royal Parrot Finches. This is because juveniles take about 20 months to moult into adult plumage and, in the process, undergo a series of temporary colour changes. It is obviously important, therefore, that the birds (or museum skins) which are being compared are at the same stage of maturation.

E. cyaneovirens cyaneovirens

The red of the head is more intense than that of *E. c regia*, while the areas of plumage which are blue in the latter sub-species are more greenish-blue in *E. c. cyaneovirens*. It occurs on the island of Upolu (Western Samoa).

E. cyaneovirens gaughrani

The head is dark red, and the blue of the nape is relatively pale. It occurs in Savai'i (Western Samoa).

The habits of only two sub-species, *E. c. regia* (from Vanuatu) and *E. c. cyaneovirens* (from Western Samoa) have been studied in any detail. There are considerable differences between them. *E. c. regia* is predominantly a fig-eater which congregates wherever there is ripe fruit, whether this is on the edges of forests, in forest clearings or in cultivated areas where wild fig trees are growing. Although it is generally a secretive bird which restricts itself mostly to the upper canopy of the rain forest, up to 30 birds may be seen feeding in the same fig tree. It exploits a variety of different figs as food, including *Ficus dicaisnea*, *F. acorhyncha*, *F. obliqua*, *F. verrucosa* and *F. kajewskii*. Its techniques for dealing with these fruits are described in Chapter 3. Some insects are included in the diet (about 20 per cent in crop contents) but it is believed that most of these are taken from fig fruits. Fruit doves and lories compete with *E. c. regia* for figs in Vanuatu and may drive them from trees.

E. c. cyaneovirens occurs in similar habitats in Western Samoa to those described for *E. c. regia* and it, too, feeds on figs. *E. c. cyaneovirens* is, however, far less reliant on these fruits; it takes a much more varied diet. The crop contents of a nestling

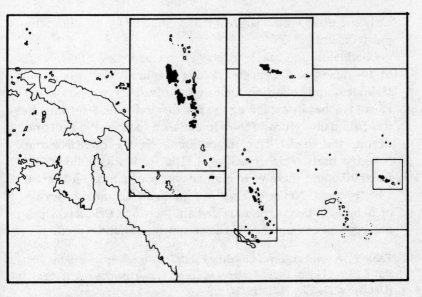

Fig. 21 Distribution of the Royal Parrot Finch. One inset (to the left) is an enlargement of Vanuatu (formerly New Hebrides); the other inset is an enlargement of Western Samoa.

examined by Ziswiler et al. (1972) contained about 40 per cent fig seeds, 30 per cent herbaceous seeds, or those of other plants, and 30 per cent small caterpillars. It prefers the seeds of introduced herbaceous plants to those of grasses.

E. c. regia usually occurs singly, in pairs or in family groups; *E. c. cyaneovirens* commonly occurs in pairs but also forms flocks of up to 40 birds. There are also differences in breeding behaviour, including timing of breeding, nest sites and nests themselves. These are summarized in Table 9.

Avicultural Notes

The Royal Parrot Finch has occasionally been kept by aviculturists, but it has never been established. This is unfortunate since early successes with it suggest that it could be bred without too much difficulty.

Goodfellow and Mayer (described in Goodfellow, 1934) went to the lengths of actually visiting Vanuatu (then the New Hebrides) and collecting their own birds. They trapped Royal Parrot Finches by exploiting the fact that individuals feeding on figs habitually return to the same branch to open the fruit and devour the seeds. They placed lime on the branches and collected birds which stuck to it. The work was tedious and frustrating and there were many days on which no birds at all were trapped. Nevertheless, they gradually acquired in excess of 20 birds in this way and added another 15 individuals which had been taken from the wild as nestlings and hand-reared.

Table 9 A comparison of breeding habits in two sub-species of the Royal Parrot Finch, *E. cyaneovirens regia* and *E. cyaneovirens cyaneovirens*. (Data from Ziswiler et al., 1972)

	E. c. regia	*E. c. cyaneovirens*
Breeding season	May to December	January to April
Nest site	Usually in lower part of upper canopy of forest. In forks of trees or among small branches	In trees, often among epiphytes or plant parasites; 6-8 m (20-26 ft) from the ground
Nest	Large and elliptical; fibres, leaves, dried grass and vine tendrils	Downward directed entrance hole; stems fibres, etc.
Clutch size	2-4	3-4
Incubation	14 days	14 days
Young in nest	21 days	18 days
Young independent	1-2 weeks	2 weeks

Since *E. c. regia* is a fig-seed eater, there were inevitable problems with diet. Goodfellow and Mayer fed their birds on fresh fig fruits, egg yolk, apple and lettuce. Eventually, however, the birds adapted to, and survived on, diets which contained the usual finch mix of seeds (full details are not given). The birds were eventually shipped back to England, where the fate of most of them is unknown.

Mr C. H. Macklin (1935) obtained a pair of them, however, and successfully bred from them. His birds were still reluctant to take canary and millet seeds but they fed on millet sprays and seeding grasses. They were also provided with soft food, meal-worms, apple, chickweed and lettuce. The pair was kept in an outdoor aviary during the summer, in a mixed collection of Cherry Finches, Cuban Finches, Aurora Finches, St Helena Waxbills, Green Avadavats, Lavender Finches and an Amethyst-rumped Sunbird. The Parrot Finches nested in a travelling cage which had been hung in the top corner of the flight, constructing the nest with grass stems, dead leaves, straw and fibrous roots. Two young hatched from a clutch of three eggs and were fed by the parents mainly on mealworms and soft food. One male youngster survived to maturity in this brood, and a female survived in a second brood.

Further breeding successes were achieved more than 30 years later by the Danish breeder Mr Dalborg-Johansen (1966). He obtained four birds in 1963 and was successful in breeding from them when they were caged in an indoor flight measuring approximately 1 m × 75 cm × 50 cm (39 × 30 × 20 in). Six youngsters were reared from three clutches. The first two clutches were placed under Bengalese Finch foster parents and the third was parent-reared. The diet provided was supplemented with a dry insectile mix, sprouted seed, chopped hard-boiled egg and grated carrot.

15

Peale's Parrot Finch,
Erythrura pealei

Fig. 22 Peale's Parrot Finch.

Peale's Parrot Finch is closely related to both the Red-headed Parrot Finch and the Royal Parrot Finch, and Ziswiler et al. (1972) grouped them together in the same sub-genus, *Acalanthe* (see Chapter 1). Adults of each of these species have bright red face masks, but Peale's can be distinguished from its relatives by a black chin, blue upper breast and bright green nape and back. Male and female Peale's Parrot Finches are difficult to distinguish, but juveniles have blue heads, paler body plumage and yellow bills (not black as in adults).

This species is restricted to islands of the Fijian archipelago. There has been massive destruction of the rain forest in Fiji, but Peale's Parrot Finch has adapted well to the consequent habitat change. It is still common and, unlike the Pink-billed Parrot Finch, another inhabitant of Fiji but one which has been less adaptable, its existence is not under threat. It lives in plantations, gardens, forest clearings and on the edges of forests. Individuals have a catholic choice of diet: rice has become a favourite food, in addition to grass seeds, such as *Sorghum vulgare, Miscanthus japonicus, Pennisetum polystachion, Isachne vitiensis* and *Cyrtococcum oxyphyllum*. Seeds of herbaceous plants, including figs, are also eaten, and so, too, are insects. The crop contents of birds examined at two different localities by Ziswiler et al. (1972) were as follows:

Nauseri Agricultural Station: 60 per cent grass seeds
                                          20 per cent herb seeds
                                        20 per cent insect larvae

Dromodromo: 35 per cent fig seeds
                                        35 per cent *Casuarina* seeds
                                        20 per cent grass seeds
                                        10 per cent insects and spiders

Birds normally occur in pairs or small flocks of four to eight, but larger flocks of 30 or so individuals are seen in rice plantations.

The breeding season is from July to August, although birds have been found breeding in February. Nests are constructed in the tops of densely foliated trees, 3-6 m (10-20 ft) high. They are globular with narrow entrances, and are constructed from fibrous material and grass stems. Three to four eggs are laid per clutch. Incubation lasts for 13-14 days and nestlings spend about 21 days in the nest. Parents continue to feed their young for about 14 days after they fledge.

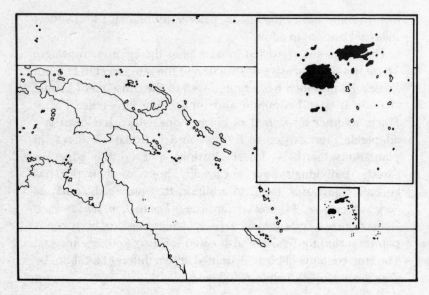

Fig. 23 Distribution of Peale's Parrot Finch. The inset is an enlargement of Fiji.

Avicultural Notes

This species was bred at London Zoo in 1912 (see Restall, 1972) and there have been many successes since then, particularly in relatively recent years. Nicholson (1962) reared young from pairs which were given small aviaries to themselves, and Langberg (1963) was successful using long cages measuring approximately 2.5 m × 75 cm × 50 cm (98 × 30 × 20 in). These aviculturists allowed parent birds to rear their own young, but Eggington (1968) found that Bengalese Finches will act as successful foster parents. Gates' (1965) experience with birds in fully planted aviaries in New South Wales suggests that they may be good aviary subjects, especially in the equitable Australian climate. As might be expected from the feeding habits of wild birds, captive individuals are prepared to take a variety of different foods. Langberg supplemented the food provided for his stock with soft food, hard-boiled egg, milk sop and vitamin additives. Eggington gave his birds food supplements in the form of brown bread soaked in milk, with added wheat germ extract, soaked seed and raw apple. Gates fed a variety of different foods, including hemp, rape, sunflower, linseed and hulled oats; the latter were preferred above all other seeds. The diet also included soaked bread, egg, apple, seeding grasses and mealworms.

In our own experience, fruit and herbaceous seeds are important additions to the diet when it is intended to bring birds into breeding condition. Our best results have been achieved with individuals which have just reached sexual maturity and may be no more than five months old. Birds which are older than 12 months are more reluctant to breed. This species is shy and timid and, even under caged conditions, never becomes fully tame. The best breeding results can therefore be expected when a pair is given a flight or large cage to themselves, situated where there will be little disturbance. Nest boxes should be placed in deep cover in the aviary. In the birdroom, paper over the corner of the cage in which the nest box is positioned, gives some seclusion. A sure sign that the birds are in breeding condition occurs when the male feeds the female. She responds by making calls like those of nestlings.

Peale's Parrot Finches are good subjects for colony breeding. The wire baskets described for breeding Katanglad Parrot Finches in Chapter 12 are, however, unsuccessful. Members of this species pull the nesting materials from them. They will use standard half-open nest boxes, positioned about 2 m (6½ ft) above floor level.

16

Pink-billed Parrot Finch, *Erythrura kleinschmidti*

Fig. 24 Pink-billed Parrot Finch.

The relationship between the Pink-billed Parrot Finch and other parrot finches is believed to be a distant one (see Chapter 1). It is a relatively thick-set species, which can be distinguished from its relatives by its large pale pink bill, black face mask and dark blue crown. The rump and upper tail coverts are red. The remaining plumage is olive-green. The sexes are alike. Juveniles

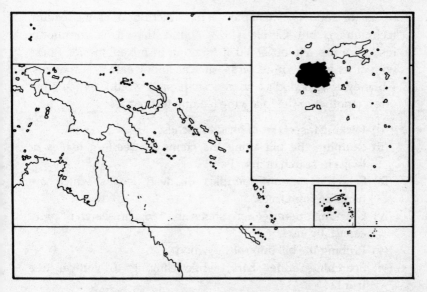

Fig. 25 Distribution of the Pink-billed Parrot Finch. The inset is an enlargement of Fiji.

are generally darker in colour than adults and the black face mask is less extensive.

This shy bird occurs only on the island of Viti Levu, which is one of the larger islands of Fiji. It was discovered by Theodore Kleinschmit in 1877, but then nothing was heard of it for about 40 years. Although several sightings were made in the mid-1960s and 1970s, it was still regarded as a rare species. Ziswiler et al. (1972) and Clunie (1973) found, however, that it was more common in some localities than had been supposed, and they were able to make observations of its habits.

Of all the parrot finches, the Pink-billed Parrot Finch is most closely associated with the rain forest. Clunie (1973) observed birds outside the forest, but in an abandoned cocoa plantation which was overgrown and rapidly reverting to rain forest. Birds were usually observed alone or in pairs, but occasionally occurred in small flocks. The species evidently has versatile feeding habits. Ziswiler et al. (1972) believed that wild figs were

99

its major food (see Chapter 3 for description of its feeding techniques), but Clunie (1973) found that it is commonly insectivorous. He observed it foraging in mixed-species flocks with other insectivorous birds, such as honey-eaters, shrikebills, white-eyes, broadbills and fly-catchers. It would switch from one to another of the following feeding techniques:

  (i) Pecking insects from dead branches.
  (ii) Running the bill along the stems of tree-fern leaves or twigs in search of insects.
  (iii) Searching among bundles of dead leaves which are hanging from trees.
  (iv) Cracking open tree-fern stems and twigs in search of prey, especially ants.
  (v) Probing the bill into rotting wood.
  (vi) Searching under bark, while clinging to vertical tree trunks.
  (vii) Searching among fallen leaves.

Clunie (1973) observed birds nesting from May to August, but since juveniles have been seen from October to January, breeding may occur throughout the year. Only one nest has been described, however. This was in a tree on the edge of the rain forest, in the fork of small branches, about 6-7 m (20-23 ft) above the ground. The nest was globular and was constructed from dead leaves, twigs, lichens and similar materials. The entrance hole was small. The eggs were described as being light red with dark red spots in early reports, but such coloration is unusual and needs confirmation.

The destruction of rain forest on Viti Levu threatens this species. There were probably no more than 300-400 individuals in 1972 (Ziswiler et al., 1972); its fate since then is unknown.

Avicultural Notes

This species is unknown to aviculture.

Bibliography

Abrahams, C. N., 'Breeding the Tri-coloured Parrot Finch in South Africa', 1939, *Avicultural Magazine*, 5th series, 4, pp. 229-33.

Carter, N. & Curry, D., *The trade in wildlife. Mortality and transport conditions*, 1987, Environmental Investigation Agency, Colvert Press.

Clunie, F. 'Pink-billed Parrot Finches near Nailagosakelo Creek, Southern Viti Levu', 1973, *Notornis*, 20, pp. 202-209.

Dalborg-Johansen, J., 'Breeding of the Royal Parrot-Finch', 1984, *The Grassfinch*, 8, pp. 104-107.

Diamond, J. M., *Avifanna of the Eastern Highlands of New Guinea*, 1972, Nuttal Orn. Club, No. 12.

Du Pont, J. E., 'Notes from Western Samoa, including the description of a new parrot finch (*Erythrura*)', 1972, *Wilson Bulletin*, 84, pp. 375-6.

Eggington (1968), see Restall, 1982.

Evans, S. M. and Fidler, M. E., *The Gouldian Finch*, 1986, Blandford Press, London.

Fry, P. A. M., 'Parent rearing of the Pintailed Parrot Finch', 1984, *The Grassfinch*, 8, pp. 12-13.

Gates, W. A. S., 'Breeding the Fijian (Peale's) Parrot Finch', 1982, *The Quill*, 6, pp. 73-5.

Goodfellow, W., 'The Royal Parrot Finch', 1934, *Avicultural Magazine*, 4th series, 12, 173-82.

Goodwin, D., *Estrildid finches of the world*, 1982, British Museum (Natural History), Oxford University Press.

Hachisuka, M. and Delacour, J., *Erythrura viridifacies*, 1937, sp. nov. Bull. Brit. Orn. Club, 57, pp. 66-7.

Horner, P. & L., 'Good viewing with Bamboo Parrot Finch', 1989, *Cage & Aviary Birds*, January 7, 1989, pp. 1-2.

Immelmann, K., *Australian Finches in Bush and Aviary*, 1965, Angus and Robertson, Sydney and London.

Karl, F., 'Lauchgrune Papageiamadinen (*Erythrura prasina*)', 1964, *Die Gefiederte Welt* 1964, pp. 2-4.

Kear, J. and Berger, A. J., *The Hawaiian Goose*, 1980, T. and A. D. Poyser, Calton.

King, W. B., 'Island birds: will the future repeat the past?', *Conservation of Island Birds*, 1985, edited by P. J. Moors. ICBP Technical Publication No. 3.

Langberg, W., 'Breeding Peale's Parrot Finch', 1984, *The Grassfinch*, 8, pp. 111-4.

Macklin, C. H., 'Breeding of the Royal Parrot Finch', 1935, *Avicultural Magazine*, 4th series, 13, pp. 245-8.

Marshall, A. J., 'The breeding and distribution of *Erythrura trichroa* in Australia', 1948, *Emu*, 47, pp. 305-10.

Mayr, E., 'The parrot finches (Genus *Erythrura*)', 1931, *Am. Mus. Novit.*, 489, pp. 1-10.

Mitchell, I. G., 'The taxonomic position of the Gouldian Finch', 1958, *Emu* 58, pp. 395-411.

Mogg, M., 'Mutations in the Parrot Finch', 1988, *The Grassfinch*, 12, pp. 17-18.

Morley, I., 'Experiences with the Green Faced Parrot Finch', 1984, *The Grassfinch*, 8, pp.108-10.

Neff, R., 'Die Papua-Papageimadine (*Erythrura papuana*)', 1970, *Gefiederte Welt*, pp. 21-2.

Nicholson, N., 'Breeding of Red-headed Parrot Finches', 1950, *Aviculture Magazine* 56, 249-52.

Nicholson, N., (1962), see Restall, 1982.

Nilsson, G., *The bird business. A study of the commercial bird trade*, 1981, Animal Welfare Institute, Washington.

Pratt, H. D., Engbring, J., Bruner, P. L. and Berrett, D. G., 'Notes on the taxonomy, natural history and status of resident birds of the Palau', 1980, *Condor*, 82, pp. 117-31.

Restall, R. L., 'An introduction to parrot finches', No. 5, Peales and Royals, 1982, *The Quill*, 6, pp. 44-7.

Restall, R. L., 'An introduction to parrot finches', No. 5, Peales and Royals, 1982, *The Quill*, 6, pp. 44-7.

Ripley, S. D. and Rabor, D. S., 'The avifauna of Mount Katanglad', 1961, *Postilla*, 50, pp. 1-20.

Savage, E., 'Parrot Finches', 1897, *Avicultural Magazine*, 3, pp. 166-7.

Van Balen, S., 'Some biological notes on the Tawny-breasted Parrot Finch, *Erythrura hyperythra'*, 1987, *Kukila*, 3, pp. 54-7.

Webb, P. B., 'Common or Red-headed and Tri-coloured or Blue-headed Parrot Finches', 1932, *Avicultural Magazine*, 4th series, 10, pp. 299-310.

Ziswiler, V., Guttinger, H. R. and Bregulla, H., *Monographie der Gattung Erythrura Swainson 1873 (Aves, Passeres, Estrildidae)*, 1972, Bonner Zoologische Monographien, No. 2.

Index

pair bond 30
Papuan Parrot Finch 11, 12, 17,
    22, 27, 76–78
Peale 11
Peale's Parrot Finch 11, 12, 14, 16,
    17, 25, 27, 94–97
perches 42
Pink-billed Parrot Finch 11, 12, 18,
    22, 25, 27, 33, 95, 98-100
Pin-tailed Parrot Finch 9, 11, 14,
    16, 17, 19, 23, 25, 27, 29, 46,
    61–64
Pratt, H.D. 25, 102

Queensland Finch Society 36, 37

Rabor, D.S. 10, 11, 79, 102
rain forest 20–21, 32
Red-headed Parrot Finch 9, 11,
    12, 13, 16, 25, 27, 32, 37, 38,
    40, 83–87, 88
reflective papillae 13, 14, 15
Reichenbach 55
Reichenowia 17
Rhamphostruthus 18
Restall, R. 63, 96, 102
Ring-necked Parakeet 36
Ripley, S.D. 10, 11, 79, 102
Royal Parrot Finch 11, 12, 16, 17,
    25, 27, 33, 40, 46, 88–93

Savage, E. 86, 103
Sclater 11
seed containers 43
seed mix 49
Silverbill
    African 37
    Indian 37
soft food feeders 43
soft food mix 50
song 12, 14, 30

Sparrman 9, 11, 61
speciation 15
Spice Finch 25, 37
sprouted seed 49
Sunbird, Amethyst-rumped 93

Taylor, E.H. 65
Teague, P.W. 74
temperature 41
trade 33, 34–35
Trichroa 17
Tri-coloured Parrot Finch 11, 17,
    27, 29, 30, 68–69

utensils 42–43

Van Balen, S. 57, 103
vermin 45–46
Vieillot 9, 11
vitamins 50
Vorderman 55

Wagner, H. 64
water fonts 42–43
Waxbill
    Orange-cheeked 37, 93
    Red-eared 25, 84
    St. Helena 37
weaning 52–53
Webb, P.B. 74, 83, 86, 87
Wildfowl Trust 35
wild-trapped birds 33
World Pheasant Association 35

Zebra Finch 32, 36
Ziswiler, V. 7, 15, 16, 18, 25, 26,
    28, 57, 70, 71, 72, 73, 75, 77,
    80, 85, 91, 92, 94, 95, 99, 100,
    103
Zosterops, Black-capped 59

Photographic Acknowledgements

Colour photographs courtesy of: Dennis Avon (plates 1, 2, 3, 4, 6, 7, 8, 9, 10 and 11); Ron and Val Moat (plate 5); all others lent by Stewart Evans.

BREEDING NOTES

BREEDING NOTES

BREEDING NOTES

BREEDING NOTES

BREEDING NOTES